My Life In The
MIDDLE OF THE MOB

C. J. Draper

cpoll123@gmail.com
phyllis@integritydenver.com

Printed in the United States of America

ISBN 978-1-7326681-9-5

First Edition

14 13 12 11 10 / 10 9 8 7 6 5 4 3 2 1

There is in every true woman's heart
a spark of heavenly fire,
which lies dormant in the broad daylight of prosperity;
but which kindles up, and beams and blazes
in the dark hour of adversity

– Washington Irving

- *The Ladies* -

It Started in Vegas

The two cousins were born in the same year, in the same hospital, delivered by the same doctor, just eight days apart. For the first eighteen years of their lives they grew up in houses that sat side by side. Then, Lena left for college on the West Coast and Samantha married and remained in North Sable; birthday and holiday cards barely kept them connected. Oh, they heard snippets of each other's lives through Lena's father, Max, and Samantha's mother, Maria, who were brother and sister and remained living next door to one another until their deaths.

When Lena's father died at age one hundred, Sami phoned her cousin to offer her condolences. After fifty-six years since they'd last seen each other, with most of their existence behind them, the two women decided to reconnect in Las Vegas, the only vacation spot of their childhood.

The long corridor with gleaming floors running through the lobby of The Linq Hotel & Casino led patrons dangerously close to the various casinos and bars to the check-in desk. The two cousins spotted each other midway. Lena recognized Samantha first, from all the family photos that her father had passed along.

Sami always looked as though she had just stepped out of a magazine article on how to age gracefully: chic hair style with no hint of gray, nails and toes manicured in bright red with lips to match, and a hint of mascara. Lena, an older version of her in her former college hippie days: no make-up, practical shoes, and comfy attire in a flowing, ankle-length flowered dress with long gray hair pinned back from her aging face. For two seventy-four–year-olds, they both looked adorable.

"Sami, Sami," Lena shouted and waved as she hobbled toward her cousin.

Samantha shouted back, "Lena, is that you? I hear you, honey, but I can't see you."

Lena left her four-wheel suitcase spinning as she threw her arms around her cousin's neck; they hugged, cried, and laughed all at the same time.

"God, Sami, you've hardly changed at all," Lena said, looking shocked. "What in the world do you do to look like this, plastic surgery?"

"Well, yes, just one face-lift and about ten gallons of Botox. "Let me look at you, sweet cousin," she said pulling her glasses out of her purse. "I should wear them at all times because I can't see my hand in front of my face without them, but glasses would make me look older," she said, as she placed them on her nose.

She examined her cousin for a few disapproving seconds.

"You're completely gray, I mean it's a beautiful silvery gray. But so… well… you know, gray. Why did you go gray?" Sami asked.

"I went to a women's retreat to boost my feminine power and a very nice lesbian told me to stop dyeing my hair because I needed to let my wisdom show," Lena explained.

"I imagine Doctor Phil would ask, 'How is that working for you?'"

"Well, I'm saving a hundred and twenty-five bucks every six weeks at the salon so I can afford to buy you an expensive drink. Come on, Sami," Lena said, "let's check these bags with the bellman and go over there," she said, pointing to the nearby 3535 Bar.

The two ladies struggled up the five steps leading to the bar and sat on the very end, as far away as possible from the sound of Lady Gaga's "*Bad Romance*" blaring through the loud speakers.

"What is it with this town, is everybody deaf?" Sami commented.

"Well, if you're not when you get here, you will be by the time you leave."

"What can I get for you two lovely ladies?" the tall, tanned, dark-haired, twentysomething bartender asked.

"What did you say?" Sami asked, motioning for the bartender to come near as she leaned in close enough to touch noses.

"I said, what can I get for you?" he repeated, smiling, and moving back an inch.

"I don't suppose you're available, are you?" Sami teased.

Samantha attempted to brush her hair back, but her

hand collided with the glasses that she had forgotten were on her nose. She snatched them off her face quickly and attempted to be coy.

"I haven't seen my cousin for fif—." She stopped the give-away number from coming out of her mouth. "A few years," she said, putting her arm around Lena, "and that calls for two double shots of the best tequila you have."

"Are you kidding?" Lena protested. "I can't possibly drink a double shot of tequila, Sami, you'll be picking me up off the floor."

The bartender reached for the Patrón Silver perched on the glass shelf, then bent over to retrieve the fresh limes.

"Isn't he gorgeous?" Samantha asked Lena, as her eyes drifted from his handsome face to his perfect ass.

"Sami, he's young enough to be your grandson for God's sake."

"Grandson? Thanks a lot. You really know how to hurt a person."

Just then the bartender set down the two double shots with a salt shaker and two limes.

"Okay," Sami said, as she lifted her glass, "come on, honey, we have to toast." Lena lifted her glass obediently.

"Here's to the seventy-four years we've had and whatever time we have left. Down the hatch."

"Sami, are you crazy? I can't swallow this whole thing."

"Sure you can. Lick the back of your hand and pour a little salt on it like this," Sami said, demonstrating, "hold your nose and drink until it's gone, then suck on that lime."

They finished the tequila simultaneously; then both

started choking and laughing alternately. Lena sneezed four times in a row, causing Sami to double over with laughter.

"What's so funny?" Lena asked, "I don't know why, but ever since I turned seventy, I sneeze after I choke. It drives me crazy," she said, laughing.

When she had recovered from the giggles and the tequila had stopped burning her throat, Samantha looked deep into her cousin's eyes.

"How in the world are you, my sweet cousin?" Sami asked.

"Okay, you asked, so let me get it out of the way and then we won't talk about it anymore, agreed? I'll start from the top of my body and work my way down. I'm getting cataracts and night driving is hazardous. I have constant sinus infections and the antibiotics caused a rotator cuff tear, and a tendon tore away from my shoulder, just one of my many surgeries. I've had five root canals in the last three years. I had a complete hysterectomy when I was forty-eight, due to a dermoid tumor that burst inside me; it was growing hair, teeth, and bones."

Sami grimaced.

"I know, don't ask. I have heart disease; my knees are shot; and the padding on my feet has worn so thin I need to wear orthotics in all my shoes. That's it in a nutshell. How in the hell are you?" Lena asked.

"Well, not that bad, honey. But then, I try not to dwell on the negative. Right now, there isn't a pain in my body; I can't even feel my face," Samantha said.

Lena touched her own cheeks and began laughing hysterically. “Me either.”

Sami ordered another round and this time they downed the shots without pinching their noses. They both agreed that the second round was amazingly much smoother than the first. The tequila left the two ladies giggling hysterically as they left the bar and headed for the Strip.

They roamed Las Vegas Boulevard until dark and ended up in front of the Bellagio fountains holding their half-empty liter Margarita glasses. Tears streamed down their faces as they watched the water dance to the voice of Luciano Pavarotti, one of the few memories they would have of that tequila-infused night. They took a taxi back to The Linq, retrieved their bags and checked into their room. The desk clerks were tittering as they watched the cousins swerving down the corridor toward the elevators and quickly sent a bellman to help keep them from hitting other patrons with their cases.

They slept soundly, well into the ten o’clock hour the following morning. When Lena’s eyes struggled to half slits to the blurry view of Sami lying in the adjacent queen bed, fully clothed, with shoes still on her feet, and wig askew, she sat up, forcing her eyes to open fully. As she glanced down at her own previous day’s attire and caught sight of her disheveled image in the mirror next to the bed, she gasped.

“Oh God!” Lena whined out loud. “How did I ever get this old?’

“We are not old, at least I’m not,” Sami said, as she

struggled up in a stupor to her own reflection. "Yuck, you're right; I guess we are a little old this morning. What do you expect after a wild night of gambling and drinking? Did we try to jump into the Bellagio fountain last night?"

"You did," Lena replied. "But the nice police officer let us off with a warning. Now that was one time our age was a big advantage." Lena lowered her head into her hands. "I feel like shit."

"Nothing a day at the spa can't cure," Sami said, lifting the phone to make reservations. "They have some sort of salt room there that is supposed to cleanse your lungs of smoke, clear your sinuses, soften your skin, and raise your boobs a few inches. What say we get thee to the massage table?"

After the steam room, Jacuzzi, and an hour's massage the two ladies helped themselves to the complimentary coffee and fruit and proceeded to the salt room. The yellow glow from a back-lit wall cast a golden hue on their skin, as their nude bodies went limp in the comfortable lounge chairs. The attendant turned on the salt mechanism and left them alone, saying she would be back in fifty minutes. Within seconds, they could taste the salt on their lips and see the light powdering of it on the dark floor.

"We do look younger already, don't you think, Lena?" Sami asked, glancing first at her cousin's body, then at her own.

"Oh yeah, right, at least twenty years have disappeared," Lena said sarcastically. "Face it, Sami, it is all in the lighting. Three quarters of our lives are over and there isn't a damn thing we can do about it."

"Okay. I know, I know, but I don't feel old," Sami said. "There is still a lot more I want to do; but, I'm struggling to erase the black hole of my past, all the years of fear, insecurity, and abuse. The memories keep playing over and over in my head like a record stuck in a groove, you know? I need to get it out of my head before I go insane."

They were silent; each in her own thoughts, then…

"You know, I have had a pretty crazy life, and I think it would make an interesting story. As a matter of fact, I talked to an author who is interested in writing a book about it. What do you think?" Sami asked.

"Well, that depends. What makes your story any different from others?" Lena asked.

"For one thing," Sami responded in a lowered voice, "I got entangled with the mafia and I feel very lucky to have survived. I know people who didn't.

Lena knew that her cousin had been dealt a tough hand but didn't really know just how tough.

"Well, I think you should go for it then. Will this writer pay you for the story or do you pay her to write it?" Lena asked.

"I'm not sure; we didn't discuss details. But I feel reluctant to open up to someone I don't really know."

Again, a long silence. Suddenly, Sami sat straight up and turned to her cousin.

"What about you, Lena?" Sami said, with excitement.

"Oh no, my life has been pretty normal, nothing terribly interesting to write about," Lena said.

"Not your life," Sami continued. "Why don't you write my story?"

"I'm not a writer, Sami. Even in college I never mastered a short story, let alone a book."

"What are you talking about? I remember you won a writing contest when we were in high school. And weren't you the editor of your college newspaper?" Sami reminded her.

"Yes," Lena admitted. "That's different from writing a book. If you have a published author interested in writing your life story—that's amazing—you go with that."

"But I don't trust her. I would really trust you. Besides, it would be a way for us to stay connected."

"Please?" Sami begged. "We could call each other on a specified night each week or email, text, and even meet up here in Vegas. It will be fun."

Lena stared into the glowing, golden wall, then slowly started to nod her head yes; her eyes drifted up toward the ceiling, then darted left to right and back again.

"What do we have to lose?" Lena asked out loud, to no one in particular. "You tell me the stories and I'll write them. When and how do we start?" she said, presenting her little finger for a pinky shake.

"Now, and from the beginning, right? No wait… the trouble started on the day I got married. My wedding introduced me to a world I would never have imagined."

Sami leaned forward, put her elbows on her knees, and placed her chin on her folded hands as the record of memories began to play again.

- Chapter 1 -
The Wedding Day

Sometimes you throw the dice and get a seven right off the bat. But when you're a nineteen-year-old virgin, Italian, and Catholic, born in the World War II era, the odds of that happening might be stacked against you. Might? The odds were stacked against me. Let's face it, where, when, and to whom you are born is a complete crap shoot that affects the rest of your days. I was born the day after the bombing of Pearl Harbor and I've always wondered if the vibes from all that negativity had any influence over the battle that became my life. My personal war started on my wedding day.

Perfect weather, not a cloud in the sky. Outside, spring had greened all the trees. The scent of lilacs that grew between my house and my uncle's, next-door, came floating through my window on a warm breeze. The sweet smell coaxed me out of bed. Butterflies in my stomach were flying in circles. God, I was so innocent. All I ever dreamed of as a kid, besides making lots of money, that is, was to be a wife and mother, keep a perfect house, and cook fabulous food for my family. In three short hours that dream would begin. I would become Mrs. Nicky Salatto.

While I was soaking in a hot tub of water to calm my nerves, Papa's words swirled through my head like a cold wind. He wasn't much of a talker most of the time, just sat on his rocking chair going back and forth, smoking cigarettes one after another. So, it was unusual for him to lecture me about anything. But during the three months of my engagement to Nicky, when Papa and I drove to work together every morning, he never shut up. I can still hear his voice.

"Babe, you're too young to get married. You have your whole life in front of you. You could do better. Marry a doctor, a lawyer, who knows, even a plumber makes good money and you'd never have clogged pipes. I know this family. The Salattos are not good people. Do you realize they have connections to the mob? And Nicky's father is the biggest womanizer in town."

When Papa's pleading didn't work, he threatened me.

"I won't even walk you down the aisle if you marry this guy!"

But, in the end he did walk me down the aisle… paid for the big wedding too.

It took an hour to apply my make-up, tease my hair into a bouffant then glide the dark red lipstick on to my lips. Nicky would swoon when he saw me, at least that's what I hoped. Over my head went the three chiffon petticoats then the white silk gown with the beaded pearl neckline. It flared out two feet and made my waist look about three inches round. Finally, I carefully set the small pearl tiara on top of my head and attached the long white veil. My three bridesmaids—Eileen, my older sister; Gina, my younger sister; and my cousin Lena—helped me by lifting all the layers of my gown to slide the blue garter around my leg. I still have a photo of that moment somewhere. God, I wonder what all that must have cost my parents.

St. Mary's church bells chimed for the ten o'clock Mass and the altar looked beautiful with the sun streaming through the stained-glass windows, the smell of fresh carnations, lilies and incense filled the air, ironically the same smell you find at funerals. You couldn't squeeze another Italian in that church… packed to the choir loft. Father Pat said those sobering words, "Love, honor, obey… till death… You may now kiss the bride." Nicky lifted my veil slowly, smiled as he looked into my eyes then kissed me so gently on my lips I felt faint. That man knew how to kiss a woman. I took his arm and floated down the aisle.

Outside on the church steps, rice flew from all directions and so did Jordan Almonds and pennies. Don't know where that tradition came from, but, back then, at all the Italian weddings, they threw Jordan Almonds and pennies with the rice. As a kid, I loved it. Through a blurry moment of congratulation kisses, hugs, and handshakes, my eyes drifted to a small girl gleefully stuffing her pockets with Jordans and coins. Suddenly, a strong feeling came over me, perhaps an instinct that I didn't want to acknowledge, and made me long to exchange places with that child.

The reception was at the Eagle Hall, where almost

all Italians in North Sable celebrated their weddings. The place had a long bar at one end, a huge wooden dance floor in the middle, and at the far end, a small stage for the musicians. We hired a popular local band, Nuncio and the Calzones. They played all the Italian favorites like "*Volare*" and the "*Tarantella*."

Everyone danced: young people, old people, some barely able to walk and little girls on top of their daddy's shoes giggling as the fathers attempted to waltz them away. Two long tables full of food lined the side walls: sandwiches, salami, pickles, chips, and the three-layer cake with the little bride and groom on top. But the most popular food on the table was definitely Mama's homemade cookies. Maria, my mom, baked for weeks: biscotti, wine cookies, bow ties, snowballs, and pizzelles. I swear she was a machine.

Nicky and I danced the traditional first dance as husband and wife to our favorite song, "*Smoke Gets in Your Eyes*." I felt so proud to belong to him. Papa cut in and pinned a twenty-dollar bill on my dress, which signaled all the other men to dance with me in exchange for a few bucks. My white wedding gown soon turned green, covered with ones, fives, and tens. In the meantime, Nicky was doing shots with his buddies and dancing with other girls, a little too closely I noticed. Then he disappeared. He wasn't at the bar, or on the dance floor.

I figured he must be in the john, so I went down the hall and around the corner to the restrooms to look for him. We bumped into each other as Nicky came out of the men's room laughing with one of the North Sable thugs, Johnny Borono, an old high school classmate of mine. Their red glazed eyes told the whole story: drugs.

Shocked, I asked, "What are you doing, Nicky?" He motioned for Johnny to leave, then pushed me against the wall and grabbed my chin. With a smirk on his face he said, "Cool it, Sami. No need to cross-examine me. Everything is okay, just having some laughs with a friend, that's all. Here's a little donation from Johnny," and he stuffed a hundred-dollar bill in my bra. "Now get back out there and play the happy bride, okay?" He shoved me toward the hall. Dazed, I tripped on my gown. He caught me and grabbed my arm hard, squeezing even more as he led me back to the main room. Under his breath, he uttered, "Are we a little clumsy?"

I felt queasy and frightened at what had just happened. As we got back into the crowd I managed to pull my arm free of his grip and accidentally elbowed Nicky's older brother, Frankie, who was standing just behind.

"Woo," Frankie said, doubling over jokingly. "You have quite a jab for a pretty little thing."

Then, looking quickly from Nicky to me, and seeing the daggers in Nicky's eyes, Frankie said, "Hey, brother, I haven't had a chance to dance with your bride," as he hauled me out onto the floor.

Frankie pulled me in tight, then whispered in my ear, "Hey, Sami, you know you're playing with fire when you make Nicky mad like that. Not nice. You shouldn't do that 'cause when my brother gets mad then I get mad and it doesn't turn out so good."

My whole body stiffened. I pulled far enough away from him to look into his blood-shot eyes. I mustered up the strength to address his bullying.

"Well, thanks for the warning, Frankie, but just how seriously should I take the advice of a junkie? You know your brother told me all about you. He's says you're nothing but an addict and a thief."

"Oh, he did, did he? You got some balls, woman. Well he told me a few things about you, too. You wanna know the only reason Nicky married you? Because your dad has a few bucks; you're just a meal ticket. Happy wedding night, Sami," he said, and left me on the dance floor, stunned, dizzy with fear, amid the swirling guests.

- The Ladies -

Phone Call, 8 a.m.

Before leaving Vegas, goals were set by both ladies and included a pinky shake on the following:

- We will write one hour a day and no less than one page a day.
- "We will get published" became our mantra.
- We will remain faithful to the truth.
- We will meet in Las Vegas to drink tequila as often as possible.
- We will continue to love one another and stay connected.

Lena: *Hi Sami, did I phone too early? Is this a good time to talk? I can call back later or even tomorrow.*
Sami: Oh no, Lena, this is fine. I've been meaning to email you; but I've just been so damn busy.
Lena: *Did you get the document with the first chapter?*
Sami: Yes, and I just loved it, honey!
Lena: *You did? Oh, that makes me so happy. I was actually afraid to send it to you.*

Sami: "Don't be silly. We're in this together. I didn't see one thing I wanted to change. Except the tragedy of the truth of it. How did I get myself in that mess?

Lena: *How do any of us get through what life dishes up? We just do. You did what you thought you had to do; you did your best. I think this project will give you some perspective and help you to not only come to some acceptance but forgiveness too, of yourself and maybe even Nicky.*

Sami: Don't count on it, sweetie, at least not Nicky. You know the old song "Unforgettable" by Nat King Cole? Well, I used to love to sing that song when I went to karaoke, only I changed the lyrics to "Unforgivable, that's what you are." I'll sing it for you sometime.

Lena: *I'll hold you to that.*

Sami: I think you need to write about our childhood too, don't you think?

Lena: *Yeah, sure, Sami, whatever you want. But I think it is important to just keep the stories coming. They don't have to be in order; just keep spitting them out. Okay? Talk to you soon.*

Sami: Will do. Bye-bye.

- Chapter 2 -

Growing Up Italian

It's baffling that my marriage lasted for as long as it did. I worshipped the ground Nicky walked on and was determined to make it work. For one thing, divorce is not allowed in the Catholic Church. But at the bottom of it all... I really believed I could change him.

My culture and childhood created a strong determination deep inside of me. The second daughter of three girls; born 9 years after my older sister, Eileen, and two-and-a-half years before my younger sister, Gina, I was "the middle" child, a southpaw and pretty smart, if I say so myself. I grew up in a poor section of town in North Sable known as "Little Italy." Anyway, mostly a happy childhood: you know, we felt secure, always had a roof over our heads, and plenty to eat.

My grandfathers immigrated to the U.S. from Italy, then mail-ordered their brides. Italian on all sides; you can bet we had plenty to eat. Mama, a typical Italian wife, did it all: cleaning, laundry, ironing, and cooking for everybody and what a great cook. Every Sunday morning, without fail, the smell of Mama's homemade tomato sauce simmering on the stove drifted into our bedroom and woke us. We would cut a big piece of Italian bread and dunk it right in the saucepan. Makes my mouth water just thinking about it. And on Sundays, we had a huge homemade pasta dinner around two or three in the afternoon: salad, homemade pasta, meatballs and sausage, garlic bread, and dessert. My favorite was Mama's chocolate cake, frosting to die for.

I remember Mama always called me "honey." But then she called everybody "honey," even a cop who pulled her over for speeding one time. She told him, "Oh honey, you don't want to give me a ticket. Do you know who I am, honey? I'm Sean O'Shay's mother-in-law, honey." Sean, a Sable detective, married my sister Eileen. Mama's "honey" tickled the officer, who tried unsuccessfully to stifle his laughter then let her off the hook with just a warning. That policeman told that story to everyone at the station. Detective O'Shay became Detective O'Honey for all who heard his tale.

Papa used to call me "peanut" or "toots." He wasn't outwardly affectionate but give him a few drinks and he would go to each of his daughters and point to his cheek for a kiss to be planted. But his drinking really bothered me. On Sunday mornings, without fail, he would walk to our local Catholic church, go to Mass then directly to the bar just a half a block down the street from our house. He drank until Mom would get mad enough to send my little sis, Gina, and me into the bar to tell him dinner was ready, and he better get home. He hated seeing his two little daughters walk in that bar and he would reprimand Mom for sending us.

A happy drunk, Papa would eat the entire meal while joking that he should "trade in his three daughters for one son or a good donkey." Not the most positive reinforcement his daughters needed to hear but still it made us laugh. After eating, he headed straight for his swing on the front porch, lay down and proceeded to vomit up the entire meal… including the chocolate cake. Oh, my mom would be so furious, saying how could he do this "every damn week." Terrified and crying, I would bury myself in the back of my closet, plug my ears with my fingers to blot out the sound of heaving. Don't know why but I could never handle sickness of any kind, especially vomiting. Nothing's changed. I'm the same today.

My dad, a "Sunday alcoholic," was also an addicted gambler; gambled on everything: sports, dog races, horse races, bowling, and his favorite in Vegas… craps. The only family vacations we ever took—when we could finally afford it—were to Las Vegas. Not enough money to fly, we would pile all five of us: Papa, Mama, Eileen, Gina, and I, into the old family car (no air conditioning) for the two-day drive across the desert, sleeping in the car overnight. Talk about misery! But when we got there, if he was winning, everything was first class. We stayed at the Desert Inn or the Sands Hotel. Hard to believe both hotels are long gone, imploded… very sad. Anyway, we even got to see dinner shows like Pearl Bailey, Dean Martin, or Sinatra. And we all got tipped. Mom got the most, and once, I saw him flip a five-dollar chip to a bellman just for opening the door.

More than once, Papa had to wire for money to get the family back home. But he worked hard all of his life, eventually owned his own optical business and did quite well financially with only a fifth-grade education. Basically, you know, a good guy with a few bad habits.

We lived in the finest house on the block in the poorest neighborhood in the city. Our house was very old but I loved it and so did everyone else on our street. It was "Grand Central Station," that's what Papa called it when he would get disgusted that too many neighbors were sitting on his favorite swing on the porch.

That old porch transformed into our theater during summer afternoon rains. It had a roll-up awning that became the curtain that hung between two white columns, and a red brick ledge that served as our stage. Two swings on the porch seated the audience, made up of every kid on the block: one white wooden swing that hung on chains from the ceiling and the other, a long-cushioned swing that doubled as Papa's Sunday sickbed. Each kid took a turn to sing, or dance, tell jokes or stories. We entertained each other for hours. Listen, I'm telling you, these damn video games today have destroyed half the fun and creativity of childhood.

On the weekends, our porch became a casino. All the Italian men in our neighborhood loved to gamble, but only small stakes on the front porch. The serious games with bigger players were held in the garage behind our house with lookouts watching for the cops.

Bar-booth, their favorite dice game, was played by

throwing the dice against our front porch door. Seven or eight men, pennies, nickels and dimes spread out in front of them, hunched around a semi-circle, threw the dice, chanting things like, "Come on, seven!" or "Baby needs a new pair of shoes," which echoed all the way down our street. If I happened to be playing outside during the gambling, and I ignored my urge to pee for too long (I placed both hands on my crotch and wiggled around to keep from leaking), my Auntie Rose would open her window and call out to me, "Sami Ann, do you have to go to the toilet? You better get inside and go, young lady!"

Then and only then would I pull myself away from the game of tag or kick the can or hide-and-seek and run to the front porch only to be yelled at by the fathers, "Watch the money, don't step on the dice for Christ sake." No kidding, I could hardly get through my own front door.

We had a swing set in the backyard. I loved to swing so high that I could touch the leaves of the cherry tree with my feet; jump off at the highest point onto the warm, soft dirt or climb the poles which offered forbidden pleasures. And we had the cutest playhouse, built by the men who lived on our block. You see, Papa bought the lumber and lay it on the ground, that being the extent of his carpentry skills. The neighbors all offered advice on how to construct it and eventually Papa just sat around smoking cigarettes and watched them build it.

Once our playhouse was completed, we needed money to stock and furnish it. I think that's when my entrepreneurial skills began to show. To raise money, I started a hobby club for the kids in the neighborhood; they would pay dues and I would give them a craft to work on, like painting rocks. Definitely ahead of my time, huh? Should have called them "pet rocks" and made a fortune, right? Every meeting we would have the minutes read, work on a craft and have refreshments always provided by the moms. In summertime, we had a lemonade or Kool-Aid stand and of course there was the annual summer show.

I'm telling you that show was the greatest! Held in our backyard, we charged the neighbors ten cents per ticket. We made all the tickets and posters by hand, then delivered them to every house within a two-mile radius. Naturally, the shows were standing room only. Our mom would hang blankets from the clothes lines for stage curtains. I still hang my clothes outside to this day, which never fails to remind me of those shows. All the neighborhood kids would provide the talent. Auntie Rose dressed up like a cigarette girl, short skirt, and somewhat sexy blouse, with a tray held in front of her by a ribbon wrapped around her neck. Instead of chanting, "Cigars, cigarettes, cigars, cigarettes," she would call out in her sexiest voice, "Old razor blades, old Easter eggs, old razor blades, old Easter eggs, get 'em before they're gone." And yes, on her tray there were old Easter eggs and razor blades. Just for laughs, a lot of neighbors actually parted with cash for a used razor blade.

With the proceeds from that show, we set aside money for the playhouse supplies and a small closing night party for the cast. The rest of the money went to a mission to purchase a "Pagan Baby." Okay, okay, don't ask me, I don't know, that's just what they called them back then, "Pagan Babies." Every year, I made the executive decision to have my name on the adoption papers because, after all, I directed and produced the show.

I would do anything to make a buck. Hah, one time I even stole vegetables from grandpa's garden and sold them to the neighbors, but there was an informant on the block and that venture got shut down real fast.

I went to Catholic school from kindergarten until my second year of high school, a pretty good student in spite of the fact that I didn't make any effort at all. If I had applied myself, I would have made straight A's, except in conduct. I always got a C or lower in that category. The head of our parish, Father Pat, would come to every classroom and pass out report cards, then make anybody stand that got a C or lower in conduct. The boys were lined up against the blackboard and slapped across the face one by one. Funny thing, a lot of those Italian boys who got slapped still turned out rotten. So much for corporal punishment. Father Pat approached each girl separately, grabbed their hair and pulled their heads all the way down and bounced it on their desk. And yes, my head got bounced a few times. Can you imagine getting away with that today?

As Papa's business grew, we moved on up the ladder from North Sable to the suburbs, to a brand-new home which seemed like a palace. The outdoor fireplace on the patio, so extravagant, definitely ahead of its time and two full bathrooms, a luxury after our entire lives thus far with just one. Gina and I still shared a room but got new twin beds. We were so excited to sleep in them we went to bed two hours early. Believe it or not, Uncle Max and Auntie Rose moved right along with us into their new home right next door and I switched to public school for my junior and senior years.

You know, rebellion is a natural by-product of the teen years, but I felt slighted by Mama because she seemed to give Eileen and Gina whatever they wanted and all I got were piano lessons. I always had to beg for everything. I wanted a horse and that was completely out of the question. Of course, now I understand why. At age fifteen, I wanted to take modeling lessons and I begged for a long time before she gave in to that. I just felt aced out of all the attention lavished on my sisters. Resentful, I cut a lot of classes at school and brought friends home to party while Mom and Dad were at work, refilling Papa's liquor bottles with water so he wouldn't notice anything missing. I started smoking and "borrowed" a lot of my older sister's expensive clothes after she left for work and without asking (Eileen worked for The Sable Post and wore a different outfit to work every day). No surprise, I was voted "best dressed" at school.

I'll never forget the night I borrowed Mom's car to go "gashing"—that's what we called it when you drove slowly down 26th Street, all windows down, no matter the temperature, while "*Twilight Time*" by The Platters blasted over the radio—all in order to meet guys. I had two silk blouses of my sister's in the backseat of the car which I intended to sneak back into her closet when I got home. Naturally, I wanted to look super cool so I lit up a cigarette for the boys to see.

What I didn't see was, the ash of my cigarette that I thought I had flicked out the window had instead flown into the back seat and burned my sister's two beautiful blouses with the added bonus of a big hole in my mom's back seat. What to do? What to do? Mom didn't even know I smoked. I made up a huge lie and told Mama that those boys on 26th Street flicked a cigarette into the open back window of her car and I didn't notice until I saw the flames. She bought my lie. I dumped my sister's silk blouses into the nearest trash can before going home. Poor Eileen searched for those blouses for months and I never revealed their final resting place.

- The Ladies -

Texting on Tuesday, 1 p.m.

Hi Lena, I'm really not liking the title,
"Middle of the Mob."

Sami, it is just a working title.
We can always change it.
Don't worry about it.

Okay, but how about something like,
"Mafia Monster"?

Monster? Really?

Well he was.

I know, honey, but I don't think that title will work.
Sounds like a horror story.

It was a horror story.

Let's keep brainstorming.
Have to run. I have a Dr. appt.

- Chapter 3 -

Close Encounter with Crime

Auntie Rose Bella and Uncle Max Bella always lived next door to us with their kids, Lena and Reggie, my built-in playmates. Max was Mom's brother and a real disciplinarian who scared me. Can't count how many times my sister and I would say, "Glad he's not our dad." But Rose and Max were Mom and Dad when our parents weren't around, whether we liked it or not. In that neighborhood, there was always someone you could turn to if you needed something. Italians lived in every house on both sides of the street and everyone knew everyone else's business. And there was plenty of business going on in our neighborhood and it was certainly not legal. Mr. Rogers would not have approved.

The "big" dice games (involving mobsters with big money to bet) took place in the garage in the back of our house. I guess I was around six years old when I had my first encounter with the crime in our neighborhood. Mama and I and my baby sister spied through half-closed kitchen curtains as Mama prayed out loud, "Dear God, please, please watch over them. Don't let them get caught." Uncle Max, who didn't actually play in those games—don't know if he just didn't want to risk the money or was too afraid of getting caught—served as lookout to warn the guys if he saw any cops.

Sure enough, the warning rang out. We could hear Uncle Max scream, "Cops! Cops! Run," as he dodged into the pathway between our two houses. But poor Uncle Max, a rather short, skinny man, ran straight into the arms of the police protesting, "I wasn't even playing." Two large officers hooked him by both elbows, lifted him off the ground and carried him away saying, "Yeah, buddy, then why were you running?"

The garage door flung open and you never saw so many men run in all directions in your life: running through the alley, jumping into parked cars, stuffing themselves into trash cans, and leaping over backyard fences. One poor heavyset neighbor, Fat Jimmy, who got stuck on a fence with the post right in his crotch, cried either because it hurt so much or because he was arrested. I cried because I saw Papa jumping fences all the way up the street until he disappeared from view.

Papa loved to tell the story of where he ended up hiding that day. In our neighborhood, nobody really had a bathroom like we know them today. In our house, for example, we had a bathtub upstairs in one of the bedrooms and the toilet and sink downstairs. Many people still had toilets outside in their cellars. Papa ended up at our neighbor Irene's house and frantically threw open her outside cellar door, quickly descended the stairs, where he surprised Irene who happened to be sitting on her toilet. Irene screamed and Papa turned his back to her and said, "Irene, shh... Please don't scream. It's just me, Al Carracci. I'll keep my back turned. The cops are after me. Please just let me stay here a minute."

Irene, who must have felt humiliated and embarrassed as she flushed the toilet and pulled herself together, roared at Dad that he needed to "go now!" She had a family and couldn't be involved in harboring a fugitive. So, Papa crept to the top of the stairs, slowly and carefully lifting the cellar door to the unfortunate view of a cop's black boots.

Papa said when he went in front of the court, the judge asked him, "Mr. Carracci, why is a nice guy like you hanging out with this bunch of hoodlums? You have your own business and you have kept your nose clean until now. So, I've decided to give you a break and let you off with a warning. But don't let me find you involved with this gang ever again. Understood?"

Well… that was Papa's version anyway. And he always told this story laughing, so I'm guessing the truth lies in there somewhere.

Years later, just before Uncle Max died at age one hundred, he divulged a well-kept secret to me. My father won $28,000 in one of those bar-booth games. Back then, that was a fortune and could have put him on easy street for a very long time. Unfortunately, Papa gambled it all away and never told Mom how much he had won.

- The Ladies -

Texting on Sunday, 9 p.m.

Hey Sami, I have to say, after I got your notes about chapters 2 and 3, I felt nostalgic. What wonderful memories.

Hi Lena, Yeah, we had a great childhood in spite of the poverty we were living in, right? I'm having 2nd thoughts about the end of chapter 3. I don't want to put my Dad in a bad light re: the $28K.

There's no bad light Sami. He's dead. Remember, all the people who knew him are gone too. Hell, the 2 of us have one foot in the grave. Stop worrying. What do you think of the title, "Funny Girl and the Gorgeous Good Fella"?

Not sure I like it. I really want the word "mafia" in the title. Am I a funny girl?

No, silly. We'll leave it as it is for now.
We can always change it later, I promise... pinky shake...
(just visualize). Get some sleep.

- Chapter 4 -
Before the Storm

My sixteenth summer was unforgettable. The only responsibility I had was getting to the Orpheum theatre at night on time for my job of ushering or working the candy counter. Even that had the added perk of seeing all the new movies free with popcorn and candy. I think I saw *Around the World in 80 Days* and *Ben-Hur* at least fifty times each.

The lazy days were filled with baby oil and sunburns, men with boats, swimming, water skiing, and feeling beautiful. My ugly duckling feathers fell off and I became a swan whose reflection in a mirror startled even me. Everyone started to notice, especially the guys at Ciron Lake, a special park on the western edge of Sable's city limits.

There is a legend surrounding the lake that Mark J. Ciron, who received a patent from President Andrew Johnson in 1866 to use the land for farming, and cattle, dug a well and accidently tapped into an underground aquifer. The next morning part of his farm flooded and was covered in water. Voilà! Ciron Lake. The area surrounding that lake was once home to the first amusement park built west of the Mississippi plus a swimming facility known as Babble Beach.

There was this atmosphere at the lake which was hard to describe: happy, carefree, fun, but sort of scary, too. The old-timers thought the spooky feeling came compliments of the ghosts or spirits that once rode the rides and swam and died in that water and haunted the lake. That water definitely had its share of dead bodies: people who had drowned in boating or ski accidents, suicides, and murder victims who had been dumped there by the mob.

All I knew was I loved going there. The view of the mountains as you glanced over the lake to the west always gave me chills, the highest peaks still tipped with snow, and the white, puffy clouds rolling across the blue sky. The Canadian geese, no matter how picturesque they looked standing together on the green grass or on the frozen lake in the winter, would shit all over the place and especially on the walking/jogging path that encircled the water. I hate to think how much shit was in the water that I accidentally swallowed when I fell off my skis.

And, speaking of shit…

I met Nicky Salatto at the lake that sixteenth summer. You see, all I had to do to bum a ski ride was show up in my swimsuit. The fact that most of the men were ten to twenty years older than me didn't seem to bother anyone. One of them nicknamed me "jail bait," but nothing kept them from flirting or teaching me to water ski.

One Saturday afternoon, there was a good-looking Italian boy just a few years older than me; dark, thick, black hair, bluer-than-sky eyes, tall, lean and sexy, riding in one of the boats that always gave me a pull. He gave me the "wop greeting." Anyways, that's what I call it. It's like Italian men are too above it all to say hello, or how are you. Instead, they lift their heads slightly (a backwards head nod) which means, "I'm too cool to actually talk to you, but I graciously acknowledge that you're present." Now if that head raise is slightly tilted to the right it means, "Come over here." I got the "come over here," signal from him. He jumped out of the boat and held up a slalom ski in one hand and two fingers with the other, which indicated, "You want to ski double?" I never turned down a pull, double, single, didn't matter.

As we sat on the dock putting on our skis he introduced himself. "I'm Nicky," he said, and before I could tell him my name he yelled, "Hit it!" to the driver and the boat took off at full speed. That should have been my first clue. I struggled to stay upright but grabbed the rope and took off right beside him. As we gathered speed he crisscrossed in front of me several times to try to make me fall over the waves of his wake, laughing and teasing like a bad little boy with perfect white teeth... gorgeous! After we circled the lake, he smoothly hopped off the ski onto the dock to talk to two girls who had just arrived as I let go of the rope and sank into the water. That was it. We didn't cross paths again for a couple of years. But little did I know—on that innocent summer day—how many waves this man, Nicky Salatto, would make me jump over in my life.

- Chapter 5 -

The Offer I Should Have Refused

My first job after graduating high school was as a teller at World Savings and Loan. Remember that prehistoric institution? Did you know that at the end of 2004 the direct cost of the S&L crisis to taxpayers was about $124 billion? Now I'm not giving the mob any kudos but, back in 1963, I'll bet the amount of money the mafia stole from taxpayers was peanuts compared to that. Anyway, I started as a teller and worked my way up to account department manager and was finally promoted to secretary to the president. My parents were proud of me and so was I.

While I was working my way up the ladder at World Savings, Nicky Salatto had been drafted, serving time in Japan with the Marines for a few years. While stationed there he spoiled himself with tailor-made suits and shirts. After his tour of duty, he was honorably discharged, that being one of the few honors he ever received.

We met again at Rocco's Inn, a popular neighborhood bar. I was eighteen and Nicky was twenty-one. Now it's one thing to be good looking but you put all those good looks, the dark hair, big blue eyes, and olive complexion, in a deep blue suit with a tailored, hug-your-waist light blue shirt, opened at the collar and it's enough to make you faint. I couldn't take my eyes off him and he noticed.

Dancing with his body plastered against a friend of mine, he winked at me over her shoulder. When Sabina returned to our table I leaned in and whispered in her ear, "He was flirting with me while you were dancing with him." Sabina, tipsy, just shrugged and said, "That's cool. Go for it, Sami. He's with a different girl every night anyway," as she took another sip from her drink.

When he asked me to dance, he immediately tried to press in close, but I pulled away and kept a respectful distance between us. His head nodded as a slight smile spread across his lips as if to say, "Okay you want to play hard to get?" He just stared into my eyes and I stared right back for the longest two minutes of my life. Then he said, "You look familiar; do I know you?"

"Well if you call a short double ski ride around Ciron Lake, when you didn't even ask my name, knowing someone, then yes… I guess you know me."

"Wait, I remember. You're "jail bait," right?"

"Well, maybe back then. Now, I'm just "trouble," I said smiling. "I don't remember your name," I said, lying.

"It's Nicky… Nicky Salatto. And yours?"

"Sami… Sami Carracci."

And so, it began. At first, he just phoned me every day for about a week, and then asked me out on our first date. I remember it was summer and I had the greatest tan; to show it off I wore a white top and skirt. Military service was Nicky's excuse for not having a job or a car and that seemed logical to me so I didn't mind that I borrowed Mom's car to pick him up. He suggested a local drive-in for hamburgers and fries. Okay, so he wasn't the romantic type but he did manage to pay the tab that night.

We talked all night, about my family, about his family. He was one of eleven, three sisters and seven brothers. He laughed as he told me about all the screaming and fighting that went on in his home, the worst between his mom and dad. "I'll never forget the time my mom hit my dad over the head with a frying pan. I must have been about six. She found out he was cheating on her with a neighbor across the street and chased him around the kitchen table with me holding on to the back of her dress to try to slow her down.

"She's screaming, 'You had to be with Rosa, with Rosa of all people?'

"'You donna know whata ya speak,' Dad yelled back at her.

"I was terrified as the blood ran down his cheeks. It was brutal. It's comical now, you know?"

He hesitated then confessed, "I think you should know right off the bat, my older brother, Frankie, has already served time in prison for assault and drugs charges." The confession shocked me, but he was not his brother, so I dismissed it.

Nicky's father was a barber and had his own shop just up the street from where I grew up. As a young boy, he used to go to his father's shop and help him sweep the floor and do odd jobs that his dad made clear were "never done right." He went on and on as I nodded my head and tried unsuccessfully to suppress the memory that surfaced. When I was about twelve, I used to walk past that barber shop to go swimming at a public park across the street. There was a boy working in that shop around fifteen years old that used to stare at me when I walked by. Way back then, I told my sister and cousin that his eyes were evil and he gave me the creeps. That boy… was Nicky.

When I drove him home that night, we sat in front of his house, not saying a word. His eyes were burning a hole through me when he reached across the seat and began stroking my hair. I felt my stomach suck in automatically like it does when you drop down the first hill of a roller-coaster. Then he gently put his arm around my shoulder and slid next to me, lifted my face and placed his mouth on mine. I knew immediately: this was the one man I could have left my family for, the man I could have left my religion for, the man I would have given my soul to that night if he asked… but he didn't. To this day, I still can't explain the hold he had on me. Maybe it was just raging hormones, but I knew this was the man that I had to have in my life.

We dated for three months before we got engaged. I never let him screw me, no matter how hard he tried. Poor guy, walked around with a bulge in his pants for months. Believe me I wanted him too, my panties were always wet.

He proposed to me over a large sausage and pepperoni pizza at Pauli's Pizza Parlor on 38th Street and we married three months later.

- Chapter 6 -
Sex

Now, you have to understand that Mama was very shy and modest, never told us anything about sex when we were growing up. I learned about menstruation from Eileen, who, at age 28, got pregnant with her boyfriend (the detective—my brother-in-law—Sean O'Shay) of ten years and had to get married. It destroyed Mama and she cried for days. So, she made up her mind to have "the talk" with me and my sister Gina, before we got ourselves in trouble. We were both in our teens at the time. She led us into the bathroom, closed and locked the door, saying she had "something very important" to tell us. "I never talked to your sister Eileen about this and I know now it was a mistake," she said, coughing and clearing her throat. Her face turned candy-apple red as she passed on her sage advice.

"Don't do it!"

Our eyes quickly slid sideways toward one another, then back to her. We nodded our heads to assure her we understood. Her head nodded too, looking first into Gina's eyes then into mine to punctuate the importance of the moment. She unlocked the door and walked out.

We buried our heads in the bathroom towels to stifle the laughter.

The only other time Mama talked to me about sex was after I married Nicky. But, let me back up. You see, we had no money for a honeymoon, our wedding night was at the Landon Hotel, part of my parents' wedding gift to us. Nicky rushed into the room, leaving me standing at the door. I buried the words "meal ticket" into a coffin of denial created by my mind in an ever-growing graveyard full of them.

"Aren't you going to carry me across the threshold?" I asked.

"You're joking, right?" Nicky said.

"No, it's a tradition. Come on."

He swept me into his arms and staggered through the door, bumping my head against the frame. He threw me on the bed, lifted my gown, then crawled on top of me. The beautiful negligee (my sister's wedding gift to me) remained in my suitcase. Petticoats thrown to the floor along with my panties, his whiskey tongue in my mouth, his rough hand squeezing my breast, his legs forcing my knees apart, his groans and roars assaulting my ears, his penis thrusting hard into my vagina, ripping me apart. He came, then rolled over and fell asleep.

I gathered my beautiful gown, wet with a pink stain of sperm and blood, and tiptoed to the bathroom to wipe up the mess between my legs; startled by my image in the mirror: lipstick smeared, fallen bouffant, and streams of black mascara running down my face, I accepted the first of many failed expectations.

Nicky knew nothing about satisfying a woman. His technique started and ended with his kiss. Sex was all about his orgasm. For the first year, I didn't even know what an orgasm felt like. Then, quite by chance, through no effort on Nicky's part, I accidentally felt that overwhelming pleasure, that heart-racing, heat-inducing, out-of-control, thrusting first orgasm. Felt like a few minutes in heaven and gave me a small understanding of why men were so crazed with sex. After that, my sexual appetite increased while Nicky's decreased because he was screwing around with other women.

Soon after I married Nicky, Mama said she had "something very important" to tell me. I noticed the candy-apple red that had crawled up her neck during the first "sex" talk had begun to flush her face again. She struggled to find the words. "Nicky told me I needed to teach you how to keep yourself clean or douche or something because he said… you smell down there." I felt like someone had just punched me in the stomach. The knockout blow came when Nicky betrayed me, when he asked Mama, "Do you know what your daughter wants me to do to her?" She wants me to go down there and kiss her and stuff. You know… disgusting!"

The words exploded inside me; blood drained to my feet; my knees gave in as my back fell against the wall. I crumbled to the floor. Tears of shame and humiliation streamed down my cheeks, I cried for a long time… so did Mama.

- *The Ladies* -

Phone Call, 10 p.m.

Lena: *Hi Sami. I have to share some new thoughts with you. Do you have a few minutes?*
Sami: Hi Lena, what's up? You sound agitated, either that or you've held your pee in for a bit too long. Which is it?
Lena: I*'m not agitated; I'm excited; but also, have to pee. Just listen. I have a dear friend, M. J. who is a family therapist. I had coffee with her this morning and was telling her a little bit about your story. When I tried to explain how much in love you were with Nicky, she was fascinated. She posed these questions: Why do women fall in love with the wrong men? Why do they see the danger of falling and jump off that bridge anyway? What makes them stay once they discover the real nature of men like Nicky?*
Sami: Good questions. I'm still not sure. You know how gorgeous and charming he was and….

Lena: *Yes, I do; He was. But it had to go deeper than that. My friend thinks that we "choose" a partner largely on an unconscious level. The whole culture that surrounded you at the time determined your choices, because humans are attracted to the familiar.*
Sami: I'm not sure I'm following you.
Lena: *The Italian macho men that lived in our neighborhood were bonded together by circumstance. Their brotherhood formed because they all came from nothing, grew up in poor neighborhoods, with little education, and few prospects for success. For God sakes, Sami, mafia members lived next door or across the street from you and appeared to be doing well for themselves. How do you think that influenced Nicky? One thing for sure, those Italian boys knew how to—and were successful at—seducing women. That skill was a source of pride for them. Allowing themselves to fall in love made them feel too vulnerable, even weak. And let's face it, Italian mothers took care of the men in their families: waited on them hand and foot, spoiled them for the next poor woman who had to deal with their "little prince." All of these influences swirled around you for many years. These were the boys with whom you grew up and went to school. Your own father, God bless him, drank every weekend and gambled far too much. You were used to men behaving like that; you saw it every day.*

Sami: I know but….
Lena: *Couple that with the main goals in life for most women at that time—getting married and having children. Would you agree?*
Sami: Well yes, but….
Lena: *Didn't you tell me that your mother always said, "Don't marry an ugly man; think of your children."*
Sami: Yes but…
Lena: *Oh Sami, don't you see? It was the perfect storm!*
Sami: Can I speak now?
Lena: *Oh… yah… sure, I'm sorry.*
Sami: My father was never abusive. He never raised a hand to me or said anything unkind. He hardly spoke to us, except on Sundays.
Lena: *I know that, Sami, but don't you see, that was part of the problem too. You were starved for male attention; that hunger led you to accept Nicky and his abuse. Add to that the teachings from the Church: you married, for better or worse—honor and obey, birth control was a sin—I can't remember if it was a mortal or venial sin— but that combination was fatal. Bottom line, you thought you could change Nicky. You took the abuse because each time you believed it would never happen again. Does that clear up anything for you?*

Sami: I don't know… I guess. Did I ever tell you that… Nicky never told me that he loved me? Never! Huh… except when he went to prison.
Lena: *Oh honey, no you...*
Sami: Wow. I didn't realize that writing this story was going to be so… painful. I have to go, Lena. I'll call you later.

- Chapter 7 -
Secrets

I worshipped the ground Nicky walked on and no one could tell me different. I had to see for myself. I closed my eyes to all the warning signs: he went from job to job, broke all of the time, no money to buy me an engagement ring (I bought it and paid for it myself), never took me to nice places, hung out with a bunch of really rough guys playing gin rummy and poker, spent more time with them than he did with me, and borrowed a ton of gambling money. Actually, the gambling felt sort of familiar since Papa gambled all of his life too, so I convinced myself that was normal.

Nothing normal about playing cards with the mob, then writing checks on an account we had previously closed, to pay them off. The gambling syndicate in North Sable was big business, financed by loans from Carlo Russo, the big boss. Frantic to pay off his gambling debts, Nicky begged me to borrow money from my dad.

"They said by next week, or else," Nicky screamed at me.

The "or else" came with a reminder in the form of a heavy knock on our door at six on a Sunday morning.

Dragging himself out of bed half asleep with me trailing behind, Nicky opened the door to the face of Big Bobby Bruisio, whose name was an understatement. Bobby extended his hand for Nicky to shake and said, "Hey, good morning, Nicky." By the way Nicky grimaced, I knew the handshake was strong. "Just wanted to catch you before you went off to Mass this morning," he said, sarcastically, making his grip even firmer. "Carlo says to remind you… Friday, don't forget, ya know?" The handshake became a vice that brought Nicky to his knees. When he released his grip, Big Bobby's fist went straight to Nicky's nose and blood poured out. That was enough to scare the shit out of me and I asked Papa for the money.

Screaming and yelling at one another became our daily exercise and Nicky used it as an excuse to leave for hours, coming home at three, four, or five o'clock in the morning, which added to my rage. His gambling, fishing trips, and new clothes took precedence over paying bills. There was no trust on my part, so I questioned him on every move he made. I'm no saint either, believe me. I can scream over most Italians and have a quick temper, so I'll take some of the blame. We were both so young and immature, both raised around screaming Italians, both trapped in a swift downward spiral, but I wasn't the one borrowing money from the mafia.

His abuse escalated. On waking, I would reach over to give him a kiss and he would pull away saying, "God you look ugly, go put some make-up on before you try to kiss me." If he didn't like the food I fixed, "You're a lousy cook. Can't do anything right, can you?" Even his "affectionate" pinches to my cheeks became rough and painful, accompanied by his, "How's my big chicken nose doing today?" referring to my Italian nose.

When I told him I was pregnant with our first child, his response? "Now you've really gone and fucked things up." I would feel hurt all of the time. Completely insecure, no self-confidence left, no one to tell and nowhere to turn, I filed it all away with the rest of the secrets in our lives and I had quite a collection. But the survivor in me still had hope and determination to make this marriage work, feeling sure in my heart that I could change him and if not… this baby would.

- The Ladies -

2nd Trip to Vegas

Sami phoned Lena to set up a meeting in Vegas; said she had something to share with her. A week later, their separate planes arrived into McCarran International Airport within minutes of one another, as Sami had carefully planned. When they spied one another, they waved frantically, running across the crowded baggage claim area into each other's arms.

"Oh, Sami, honey, isn't this fun?" Lena exclaimed.

"Yes dear, I still can't believe we are doing this."

They started giggling out of sheer excitement as they retrieved their luggage.

Outside the 105° temperature hit them like a blast from an inferno and the cab line was as long as you might imagine the entrance to hell would be.

"How could this many people arrive in one city at the same time?" Sami said under her breath.

"If we ever manage to survive this line we're heading directly to the 3535 Bar and the first round is on me," Lena offered.

"I'll take you up on that," Sami said. "And if our book doesn't sell we're coming back here and selling iced water at the top of this damn line. We'll be rich in no time."

Once they reached The Linq, they had their usual shot of tequila, which brought the silliness that always followed. Then Sami announced that they were going on a field trip.

"Field trip, here in Las Vegas?" Lena inquired.

"That's right," Sami said. "A surprise I wanted to share with you."

"Whatever you say, cuz, love surprises. Where are we going?" Lena asked.

"I found out that many years ago, in the fifties, there was a notorious mobster named Eddie Trascher who owned a bar at the end of the Strip called Ringside Liquors. In 1962, a man named Dino purchased the bar, renamed it Dino's Lounge and it's still going strong after all these years. We are going to go there and have a drink. Call it a research project for the book."

"But is it safe for two old ladies to go to some random bar in Vegas?" Lena asked concerned.

"How would I know, I've never been there before. But, it won an award for Best Dive Bar in Las Vegas. Hey, we have each other. We're strong, we just need to put on our gangster faces," Sami said, as she pulled Lena off the bar stool and herded her toward the door.

"Sami, what if I don't have a gangster face, just this ancient one and it shows fear easily?"

"Oh, come on girl, we're going," said Sami as she hailed the cab.

When they arrived, they were greeted by a large sign out front:

DINO'S THE LAST NEIGHBORHOOD BAR IN LAS VEGAS

Old orange brick surrounded the lower half of the building while the top half was gaudily wrapped in a cherry, corrugated tin. It appeared to be untouched since the sixties and seemed shoddy compared to the beauty of the hotels on the Strip. The main entrance stood with one of its two red double doors open. However, that didn't make Lena feel any more welcome. Upon entering, Lena's mouth dropped open when she read the first sign she saw:

COME IN FOR A STIFF ONE.
IT'S LADIES NIGHT EVERY NIGHT.

A small raised, semi-circular, stage-like platform with plenty of room in front for a dance floor was highlighted by small ceiling lights and a sign on the wall behind that read:

GETTING VEGAS DRUNK SINCE 1962.

Just to the left stood a DJ station, with a large jar of bills and a sign warning:

I PITY THE FOOL WHO DOESN'T TIP DANNY G!

The ladies found the last unoccupied table, sat down and ordered margaritas. Sami noticed a menacing deer head with tall antlers mounted on a wood pillar with its head cocked to one side, mouth open, looking directly at them.

Sami nudged Lena and pointed up at the deer. "He looks surprised to see us."

"More like horrified," Lena retorted as they clinked glasses and downed the first of three margaritas.

The bar vibrated with loud music and too many inebriated people shouting over it. The ladies couldn't help but "people watch."

"From the looks of things, I'll bet you get drunk automatically when you pass through those red doors," Lena said, observing two men in leather pants and open vests adorned with tattoos on their chests and arms, trying to play pool but unable to steady themselves with their cue sticks.

A couple dancing to "*Somebody to Love*" looked more like they were having doggie-style sex standing up. Sami whispered into Lena's ear. "The only thing preventing those two people from having actual intercourse are their jeans. Should we yell, 'get a room'?"

"Oh my God, look to your left," Lena said. An elderly, heavy-set version of a bad Marilyn Monroe lookalike in a white halter dress, plunging neckline (fashioned after The Seven Year Itch) and a platinum blonde wig slightly askew, undulated to the music with her eyes closed, as her withered red lips whispered, "Oh… Ahh, Oh… Ahh."

"See, we're not so bad-looking after all, are we?" Lena asked Sami as the two of them stared dumbfounded at Marilyn.

Suddenly the music stopped. Danny G, the M.C., stepped up to the microphone and announced it was karaoke time.

"Who's going to start us off tonight?" Danny G asked. "Come up and sing your favorite song. If I don't have the music you get a free drink. Come on, who's going to challenge me?" When no one volunteered he started it off himself, singing "*Mr. Bojangles*." The crowd loved it and Sami and Lena were impressed with his voice and stage savvy.

Next, a couple attempting to look like Sonny and Cher (only he had a pot belly and she had dark roots with long, blond hair) gave their rendition of "*I've Got You Babe.*" The crowd went wild with applause even though they were awful.

"That's the act to follow; nothing could get worse than that," Sami said as she stood up. "Lena, this is the surprise I wanted to share with you," and she strolled up to the small stage, put a ten-dollar bill in Danny G's jar and asked him to play "*Unforgettable.*" As the intro started Sami took the mike into her hands and announced that she was dedicating the Nat King Cole song to her ex-husband—without love. That line got a laugh and the crowd's attention.

When Sami's voice floated over the crowd, Lena got chills and tears in her eyes. The crowd was mesmerized by the talent of this sophisticated senior citizen, not to mention the humor she brought with her own lyrics.

UNFORGIVEABLE

Unforgivable, that's what you are
Unforgivable, you left a scar
Like a pile of trash that clings to me
How the thought of you does things to me
Never before has someone been more

Unforgivable, in every way
And forever more, I'll make you pay
That's why, Nicky, it's regrettable
That someone so darned un-incredible
Thinks that I am unforgivable too

Dino's audience erupted in applause and gave a standing ovation. Danny G, shaking his head looked toward the bar, ordered, "Give the lady with the velvet voice a drink on the house!"

- Chapter 8 -

Baby Tina

Three weeks after we married, Nicky got fired from his job. Losing low-paying jobs became routine for him. I mean, what do you have to do to lose a retail job in a paint store, or selling shoes, for God's sake? Shortly after our wedding, our apartment was robbed, cleaned out of every wedding gift and Nicky's expensive clothes. We discovered later Nicky's brother Frankie, desperate for drug money, had done the deed. After that heist, with very little left to run a household, we moved in with my parents. I worked full time until the day my water broke.

Our beautiful daughter, Tina, was born nine-and-a-half months after our wedding. It was a long labor, 19 hours, and Nicky managed to stay with me for about six of them. His chin dropped to his chest several times while he sat snoring in the chair next to my hospital bed. I told him he didn't have to stay, hoping he would. But, of course, he jumped at the chance to leave.

I struggled through that night alone, except for the kind white-haired nurse who came running to hold my hand through every labor pain. About five that morning, exhausted and delirious, I told her that I absolutely could not give birth and to call my doctor to come and stop my labor. Patiently, she explained that wasn't possible and assured me I could deliver this baby. "Okay," I said to her, "then on the next contraction I am going to scream!" She encouraged me to go ahead and do just that. At the height of the pain I yelled at the top of my lungs then passed out. As I came to, she gently whipped the sweat off my forehead and asked, "Did screaming help?" I burst into tears, "No, no, it didn't help, not at all." She calmly patted my arm and in her sweetest voice said, "Okay then, dear… next time… don't scream."

My beautiful Tina arrived in the world at seven that morning. In those days, one had the luxury of staying five days in the hospital to heal after giving birth. The heat lamp on the episiotomy... priceless. The husbands of the other three women in my ward brought flowers and visited long hours, cooing over their bundles of joy. Not Nicky; I started to worry. There were no flowers, no fawning, no appreciation for this beautiful healthy child or what I went through to have her. Nicky came, he saw, he left—returning five days later to bring us home.

During that hospital stay, our babies were delivered to us from the nursery for feeding. How odd it felt to listen to the words of the nurse as she placed the babies in the rightful mothers' arms, repeating the same chant to each: "Here is your baby, your bottle, and the pill to dry up your milk." Seemed like I was in a scene in some sci-fi movie. Being the only woman breast-feeding in that hospital ward, I got to have Tina for the night feedings too, while the nurses took care of the bottle-fed babies themselves.

My milk dropped fast and painfully—felt like someone over-injected both boobs with cement. I needed relief and yearned to hold Tina in my arms. How special it felt: the darkened room, the other moms fast asleep, the small night-light over my bed shining on this tiny miracle. She already knew how to suck and took to my nipple with such ease: well… for her maybe. I was filled with overwhelming joy. She cast a spell over me and I fell instantly and totally in love. I just knew in my heart, with time, Nicky would too.

- *Chapter 9* -

Hope Rises and Falls

Tina finally did have an impact on Nicky. The beautiful, blue-eyed, blond cherub crept into his heart. Her smiles and giggles softened him in ways I never could and for a few years we seemed like a real family. We saved some money and with a loan from Dad, we purchased our first house: a two-bedroom, 800-square–foot single family home. A relative on Papa's side owned a meat packing plant and gave Nicky a full-time job with promise of a promotion and a higher salary. For the first time in our lives, I stayed home and played house, getting pregnant almost every year. My brother-in-law Sean, the cop (and later detective), Eileen's husband, teased me constantly, "Gee, Sami, do you and Nicky have any idea what is causing this?"

Nicky fixed the front porch, the fence, and painted the house inside and out. I was in my element, cooking, cleaning, taking care of the kids and trying to make Nicky happy. The house ushered in a somewhat normal family atmosphere, even though his late nights continued to cause major fights.

Our second child, Donny, was born when Tina was

almost two, followed by Katy a year later, and, finally, Sonny a year after that. We had four kids in five and half years. But it was Katy, our third child, who forever changed life as we knew it. At birth, Katy had a slight deformity, seven toes on one of her little feet. Although the toes had bones, they weren't connected to the ankle and the doctor assured us it was, "Nothing to worry about; this is more common than you might expect. It's an easy fix." He assured us everything else was normal. "Your baby is just fine."

We wanted Nicky's mom to see the new baby, so on the way home from the hospital, we stopped off at her house. She took one look at that foot and accusingly said, "What were you two doing to cause this?" Those words were the fertile soil in which my garden of guilt began to grow. She never visited or asked about Katy after that day.

When Katy was six months old, the two toes were surgically removed without complication. I noticed throughout her growth that she was progressing slower than our other children but, again, I was assured she was within normal ranges for her development.

On Christmas Eve, just after her second birthday, Katy dropped to the floor and started shaking. I fell to the floor and tried to hold her but her little body turned blue. Nicky hollered for me to call emergency. Barely able to keep my hands from shaking, I dialed the phone.

"Open her mouth and check to see if she is choking on something," the responder instructed.

As I knelt beside her, white foam oozed from her mouth. I turned to stone. Unable to move, Nicky pushed me aside screaming, "Open her mouth for God's sake!" He tried to force her lips apart, but her jaw was locked down. Her muscles stiffened, and she suddenly stopped breathing. When the ambulance arrived, my paralysis gave way to uncontrollable shaking. Then, as if nothing had happened, Katy regained consciousness sat up and began playing. At the hospital, they ran her through a number of tests and checked for neurological damage: they found none and sent us home saying, "If it happens again, bring her back for further testing."

It happened again the next day, on Christmas morning, and once again I panicked, unable to move at first, and then the uncontrollable shaking. We rushed her to the hospital and the testing began. Over and over again, the tests came back normal. But nothing resembled normalcy as Katy began having forty or more grand mal seizures a day.

Our lives became a nightmare. The sight of the tongue depressor in our bathroom cabinet made me queasy. The sound of Katy dropping to the floor—hitting her head or arm or whatever, on the furniture, blood everywhere—unbearable. Sometimes, I would freeze in another room, unable to go and help my baby, plugging my ears to block out the sounds of her gasping for air. Nicky stayed away more and more as I deteriorated. Every doctor was puzzled, every test, "normal," no diagnosis and no medication would stop the nightmare.

Nicky and I separated on and off during my unraveling. He didn't understand why I became paralyzed with each seizure. My mother and sisters didn't understand, but then neither did I. Once, Nicky slapped me to snap me out of the frozen state. Then one slap became two, pushing me against the stove in the kitchen yelling, "What is wrong with you?" His closed fist landed on my eye. The pain sent me scurrying to escape but he caught me by my hair and dragged me to the living room, where Katy lay on the floor seizing. He threw me down next to her. "This is your child," Nicky hollered, "you need to take care of her!" His final blow was a kick to my behind and I lay there sobbing as I heard his car's wheels squeal away. I don't know how long I lay there watching the foam from Katy's mouth drip onto the carpet. I couldn't move until she gasped for air and finally opened her eyes. I phoned Eileen and begged her to come over.

I barely managed to care for my other children. Each day started the same: my eyes opened, feelings of guilt rushed in like I had done something very bad but couldn't recall what—then, the horrible dread—when I remembered my very sick baby. And another day began amidst the thousands that followed, of me living in fear of my own child.

- The Ladies -

Texting on Friday, 12 p.m.

Good morning, sweetie! Hope all is well. Lena, I'm still thinking about titles. What about Mobster Monster?

It's the "Monster" part I don't like. How could Nicky be a monster and the father of your beautiful children?

Children, schmildren. He was an asshole. Wait until you hear the entire story, Lena. You're gonna hate him, I promise.

Okay, okay, I'll promise to try to hate him; and you promise to try not to hate him. You'll feel better, I promise.

- Chapter 10 -

Time to be Afraid

With our limited insurance plan, we searched for years for a cure, or at least a way to stop Katy's seizures. Seeing doctor after doctor, trying one medication after another until Katy—filled with drugs—became hyperactive. The "terrible twos" stretched into her teens. If you're familiar with the story of Helen Keller and her teacher, Anne Sullivan, you have an idea of what a day with my daughter entailed. She never learned to speak except for a few words that only we understood. She never grew out of the diaper stage. She needed help with all the major activities of daily living. Add to that her grand mal seizures and perhaps you can begin to understand my resulting illness... or not. Mama became a main source of support, but even she could not understand me.

"It's ridiculous. What are you afraid of?"

"Mama, I can't do this." I said, crying.

"Stop being silly. Of course, you can. You have the rest of your family who rely on you. There's no time to be afraid. Snap out of it!"

"Please try to understand. If they can't stop the seizures, I may have to place Katy somewhere else."

"Oh, dear God, Sami, don't say such a thing," Mama screamed. "Please God, forgive her. This family will never, never put one of our children in a home. Don't you even think about it. Do you hear me?"

Once, when Nicky beat me up for not being able to respond to Katy during a seizure, I begged my older sister to take me to the hospital, not for the beating, but to be admitted to the psychiatric ward. After all the red tape of getting admitted into the ward, I noticed a tongue depressor attached to the hospital room wall. I reacted to it like a kid would to the monster under the bed; only this monster was real and staring right at me from the wall. I began to feel nauseous, dizzy, and my entire body began to shake.

"Eileen, get me out of here. I can't stay here. Please I can't be here. This was a mistake," I cried.

My fear escalated into a full-blown panic attack. The drugs the nurses struggled to inject swept me into a deep sleep and I awoke twelve hours later. Blinking, I struggled to lift my lids, finally able to focus on Eileen's face and the tongue depressor beyond.

"How are you feeling?" she asked quietly.

"Please, Eileen, I can't stay here. I need to leave now," I pleaded, feeling the panic growing inside of me again.

"I think you need to stay, Sami. At least until they evaluate you further," she said.

"You don't understand. I can't stay here! Do you hear me? I need to go now," I screamed, flinging the blankets aside and jumping out of the bed.

In the car on the way home, Eileen scolded me again. "It was a mistake leaving the hospital, Sami. If you can't handle Katy and you won't take the steps to help you do it, then put Katy in a home and stop bothering everyone."

Those words felt as painful as Nicky's beating. Eileen made it crystal clear to me that no one would ever be able to understand what I was going through.

- Chapter 11 -

Dumb and Dumber

When the years of counseling failed to ease my fears of Katy's seizures, I finally went on anti-depressants. Still, my goal each day became the challenge to never be left alone with Katy. I began to rely on my oldest daughter, Tina, still a child, to help look after her younger siblings. Nicky sporadically showed up, sometimes spending the night, sometimes not.

We knew it would take big money to get Katy into better clinics. Money that we didn't have. Nicky managed to continue working at the meat plant for the next four years while using that office for bookmaking. I begged him not to do it but he reasoned it was the only way to come up with the money we needed to pay Katy's mounting medical bills and his own gambling debts.

He was desperate to pay Carlo off when he pulled his dumbest stunt. I had not seen or heard from Nicky for about four days. He showed up unshaven, dark circles under his eyes and smelling like he needed a shower.

"Where in the hell have you been, Nicky? I was worried; you could have at least called."

"I stole a shipment of meat from work."

"You did what? Are you nuts Nicky? You're going to lose this job."

"Yeah, well it's done so… you know… can't change what happened now. Relax."

"How did you pull this off?"

"It was kinda clever. I looked on the books and saw that there was a huge shipment of meat going out on Friday. So, on Thursday night, we bribed the guard at the storage yard to tell us which reefer held the shipment of meat, we drove a big rig in there, attached it, and drove away. It was so smooth."

"Who is '*we*'?" Sami asked, disgusted.

"Borono and me, we work good together, ya know? At first Johnny drove and I rode shotgun holding the rifle. Johnny drove so slowly, I got nervous, started changing the radio stations every minute and he whips his cap off and hits me in the face; tells me to cool it because I was driving him crazy. My knees were like pistons, I couldn't hold them still.

"So, Nicky, do I have this right? You're carrying a gun, in a stolen rig, with a reefer full of meat taken from the company that has kept you employed for the past four years?"

"We had a good plan, Sami; we had a contact in Vegas, all we had to do was get it to them and collect the money; it was supposed to be easy. But, when it was my turn to drive, I waited until Johnny's head fell limp and his snoring steady then I pressed the pedal to the floor; got that rig up to eighty-five. I needed to pee, so I tried to slow up; that's when I realized the brakes were out. I stared to scream, 'Johnny, Johnny, wake up! I can't stop.' Johnny yelled for me to try the emergency brake but that didn't work either. Like a mirage in the desert, the sign, **WEIGH STATION AHEAD**, popped into view. I steered that baby straight up the runaway truck ramp, and it came to a complete halt at the top and made a slow descent backward to level ground. For a few seconds we sat frozen, then glanced at each other shaking our heads. How lucky could we get?"

"What then?" Sami asked unimpressed.

"We got the hell out of there fast," Nicky explained.

"What did you do with the meat and the rig?"

"We left it. I dumped the rifle in some bushes."

It took them four rides and twenty-eight hours to get back to town. With his fingerprints all over the rig, Nicky lost his job at the meat packing plant; but because the owner was a friend of the family he didn't press charges.

My husband was now out of options, owing money to the biggest mafia boss in the state, Carlo Russo. Russo gave Nicky one option, "You're gonna pay your debts by doing me a few favors. If you perform good, you might make a few bucks for yourself." The more deeply involved in the mafia that Nicky became, the more I noticed just how dumb these North Sable Italians were. I think of them now as "the gang that couldn't shoot straight."

One day, Nicky pulled up in front of our house. As I glanced through the curtain, I noticed a red lion sticker in the back window of his car.

"What's with the red lion in the window, Nicky?"

"Carlo said it serves as a sign, so they know where you are, and what side of the city you're from. If you live west of Central Boulevard, the lion's head faces the driver's side. If you live east of Central, the head faces the passenger side. Just makes things simple."

"Simple? Simple? Don't you mean simply ridiculous?" Sami asked laughing. "What if the little lion's head is turned to look out the back window with a ferocious snarl on its face; does that mean you're on your way to knock somebody off?" I asked, sarcastically.

"I should get you one, huh?" Nicky said. "Then I'll be able to tell where you are just by driving by."

"No lions for me, thank you." By the way Nicky, don't you think by now the mob should already know on which side of Central Boulevard you live!" Nicky pondered this but gave no reply.

- The Ladies -

Wake-Up Call, 7 a.m.

Lena knew better than to call Sami before 8:00 a.m. She let the phone ring for the sixth time; Finally, Sami picked up.

Lena: *Hi, Sami. Sorry to call so early. Did I wake you?*

Sami: No… yes… okay, I had one eye open. What's up, dear?

Lena: *Well, I just finished editing Chapter 11, "Dumb and Dumber." You remember it, right?*

Sami: Of course, I remember it. I lived it.

Lena: *Uh... of course you did. Thing is, if ever there was a section where an agent would holler, "Bullshit," it's this one. And you know how we've been chanting, "We will get published" daily... uh...? I just don't want to jeopardize it by having something that would get questioned, you know what I mean? It really is pretty hard to believe.*

Sami: Well, what can I tell you? That's why I called them "the gang that couldn't shoot straight."

They really couldn't. Dumb, dumb, dumb, all of them! The schemes they came up with were pathetic. And the whole red lion thing, I'm pretty sure they were all on drugs when they came up with that ridiculous idea. Anything else, honey? How do you manage to time our calls when I really need to go to the john. Is it a sixth sense or something?

Lena: *Yeah, I feel it come over me and a message, like a ticker tape, rolls across my brain, 'now... call right now!' Okay, okay, I'll leave this chapter in, and being that it's true and all, it certainly doesn't do anything to raise my expectations for the intelligence of men.*

Sami: Hey, maybe we'll get lucky and any potential literary agent already has lower expectations. For sure, Lena, you need to take yours down a notch or two. That's a guaranteed takeaway from this project, don't you think?

Lena hung up the phone a little disheartened. Her hippy-dippy days had left her with the desire to aspire to something higher in her writing. But she returned to her computer muttering a new mantra under her breath: "Lower expectations, lower expectations." She sat down. She plowed on.

- Chapter 12 -
Katy

Months and years flew by like calendar pages blown by the wind; Katy grew into her teens, but never outgrew her child-like appearance.

She carried her small frame with difficulty, limping from the surgery on her foot. Her blond hair and blue eyes mimicked her older sister's, but she always appeared to be about ten years old. No medication could stop the seizures. She no longer had fifty a day, and many of her seizures happened at night while in bed, which prevented a lot of the accompanying injuries. I guess we will never know for sure if it was the meds or the seizures that retarded her growth not only physically, but mentally as well. At age thirteen, she had the capacity of a toddler.

Every day started the same: I slipped Katy's wet diaper off along with her pajamas and the bedding, which usually got drenched. Katy expressed her gratitude with, "Ho, ho, ho," as she rubbed my back in circles which meant, "I love you." Next, I loaded the washing machine for the first full load of the day and bathed and dressed her. On the rare occasion when the diaper hadn't leaked all over everything, I danced a celebration dance around her bed and she laughed and clapped her hands. True happiness, believe it or not, can be equated to a diaper that hasn't leaked.

More alert and active in the morning, Katy (always with a smile) demanded her "Ohs," her word for Cheerios. I would set the box of cereal in front of her and pour out just a few in her bowl. Her body jerked forward and her head bowed with approval. "Dare," was her attempt to say the word "there." "Dare" also meant that everything was okay and she was happy. Then she asked for "co" (her word for cold milk). Her final request, at least in the morning, was "chee," translation, "cheese." If you missed giving her any one of these things she had the persistence to say, for example, "Ohs" over and over again until she wore you out. One day I attempted to break the "Ohs" habit and I said, "Not this morning, Katy. No Ohs. You don't eat them anyway, sweetie."

"Ohs," Katy continued, followed by "Peez" as she smiled and bowed her head. I gave up by noon, as she had repeated her mantra every few seconds in the same steady pattern and low voice until I thought I would lose my mind. Persistence definitely works.

"Okay, okay, Katy, here's your damn Ohs. Now please, honey, stop."

She hardly ever ate any of her breakfast except for the milk; she downed that by the gallon. She would pick up one of her Ohs and touch it to her head or nose, then smile and say "Dare," and throw it down on the table or floor; it rarely went into her mouth. There had to be a fork and spoon on the table at all times, yet sometimes she wouldn't eat solid food for days, which added a whole new level to my worry. Her favorite stuffed animals had to be present at the breakfast table. If a drawer or cupboard door were accidentally left open, look out! She didn't know her own strength. She would get up and push me aside like I was a feather, pulling me off balance, and slam them shut saying, "Dare." Funny thing: she did make us laugh with all of her quirks, but I'm convinced these rituals were the only control she had.

She was happiest in the morning and never complained, even when she was sick or injured. After breakfast, the first of her four daily cocktails of pills had to be given. Within half an hour after Katy took the meds, her smile gave way to a sober face—her eyes became heavy in a dull stare—and her morning glow, gone. Then, no matter what you tried to say or do for her, the answer was always the same, "Uh-uh," as she shook her head no and turned away from me to make me disappear.

Day in and day out, just the necessary morning chores that Katy's care required, left me exhausted and I had three other children to attend to. Once I had got them all off to school, I watched the clock until Katy's nap time. By then, I needed a drink to face the endless day of chores still ahead, to mask my fear of the next seizure, and to face the dread of knowing it all had to be repeated "tomorrow and tomorrow and tomorrow."

- The Ladies -

Evening Email, 9:29 p.m.

From: Sami@hotmail
To: Lena@gmail
Subject: Embarrassing Moment

Hi Lena,

I know this is really random, but I just remembered a story I wanted to pass on to you. You said, "Spit them out," so here I go.

I just remembered a really embarrassing moment that happened to me when my oldest daughter, Tina, was in high school. I was at home alone with the kids. It was around 9:30 p.m., and the last time I noticed her, Tina (now a beauty with long, blond hair, her father's violet-blue eyes, and a figure that made heads turn) was sitting at the kitchen table doing her homework. The other kids were in bed already. It was just that time of night when you feel calm, safe, and secure in your castle, be it ever so humble. I don't know where Nicky was, but then I rarely did. He wasn't living with us at the time; for sure, he wasn't home.

I decided to get a jump on my chores and started to clean my bathroom. When it came to the shower, the best way to clean it was to get in it. So, I took off my clothes and donned a shower cap, so my hair wouldn't get wet, and proceeded to turn the water on and get in. I washed down all the walls and floors then took a shower myself. When I got out I thought, might as well clean the toilet and get that out of the way. I got the toilet brush and swished the cleanser around the bowl. Then I figured, while I am at it, I may as well go clean the kid's toilet too.

Still naked with shower cap in place, I held the toilet brush in one hand, opened the door with the other and stepped out into the hall. Suddenly, I heard a male voice. I whipped my head toward the kitchen and saw Tina, still seated at the table. Only now, so was her boyfriend, Scott. Our eyes met and for a brief moment, my heart and the universe stopped.

As if I could possibly normalize this moment, I purposely turned my head, (did not run or scream) and walked casually across the hall and into the bathroom and closed the door softly. After turning on the light and seeing the reflection in the mirror of my arm holding up the toilet brush, the shower cap on my head and my oh so naked body, I turned my back on this cartoon version of the Statue of Liberty. As the blood drained from my head, I began to softly bounce it against the

wall and wondered, Oh God, how long will I have to stay in here? After what seemed like an eternity but was only a minute or two, Tina came down the hall calling out my name with the most horrific sound in her voice.
"MOM!"

We played the blame game: "Tina, when did he get here? Why didn't you tell me he was here? And what was he doing here so late?"

"Mom, he just stopped by. I thought you were in the shower-why were you walking around naked with a toilet brush? MOM!"

We never spoke of this again, and Scott never mentioned it to Tina. When I told Nicky what happened, he laughed his head off.

If I ever ran into Scott today, in my old age, I'd have to invite him for a coffee and a chat. You know, just to see if the vision of me, naked with a shower cap on my head and a toilet brush in my hand, had affected the rest of his life. If you can't use this story, that's fine. Just had to tell you about it.

- The Ladies -

Email Reply

To: Sami@hotmail
From: Lena@gmail
Subject: Re: Embarrassing Moment

Oh my God, Sami, first laugh of the day. Yes, definitely coffee and a chat. Can I come too?

- Chapter 13 -
The First Arrest

A year after Katy got sick, things started to really get crazier. Neither Nicky nor I knew which way was up. We were breaking up and making up every few weeks. But the fireworks really got started when Nicky and Johnny Borono worked at one of the mafia bar and restaurants called Luigi's. Johnny taught Nicky to bartend, but that was just a cover for the jobs Nicky did for Carlo. The restaurant also served a second function as the money drop-off for illegal betting. Nicky received the overstuffed envelopes and Johnny transported them to Carlo after closing each night.

When we were apart, I didn't get a penny from Nicky. If it hadn't been for my father-in-law, Joe, I never would have. I will always be grateful to my father-in-law for forcing Nicky to give me cash when we were split. Nicky almost made me die laughing with his imitation of his dad coming in the bar to pick up that money. He would go to the bar on payday and tell Nicky, with his broken Italian accent, "You give-a-me money for Sami and-a your kids. Whatsa matter for you?" In good times, Joe would often say to me, "You take-ah your kids and a comma liva with me." But of course, I knew better: my mother-in-law would never have allowed that after all the kids she had raised.

During one of our marital time-outs (I think it was Labor Day), Diane, my neighbor from across the street, and I were in the backyard having a glass of wine and watching the kids play. She didn't have children of her own and adored mine. We spent a lot of time together because she was kind enough to come when I wasn't able to handle being alone with Katy. When I think back, I don't know what I would have done without her.

Nicky showed up at the house and swept in with his usual charm.

"What are you two beautiful ladies up to today?" he said, flashing that irresistible smile. I knew him by now and that approach always preceded a request.

"Sami, I need you to move your car to the street. I'm going to need the garage for a while."

"What do you need it for?" I asked.

"I'm going to store some stuff in there."

"What do you mean? What kind of stuff?"

"It's nothing and I'll have it out by next week, I promise."

"This is my house and I have a right to know what you are putting in there, Nicky," I insisted.

"It's none of your goddamned business. Now just take your car out," he demanded, raising his voice. "I may not be living here, but I still own part of this house too and now I'm going to put something in my garage. It's that simple."

An hour later, he arrived with two huge U-Hauls and hired kids in the neighborhood to help him carry the large boxes, which he stacked to the ceiling. After locking the garage door with a new lock, he left for another load, saying he would be right back. Diane and I immediately investigated, peering through the windows to attempt to read what, if anything, was written on the boxes. The small print on the boxes was too difficult to make out, but the word "Italy" in bold print caused both of our jaws to drop and I gasped.

"I'm guessing whatever is in those boxes came across a few borders. What do you think, Sami?" Diane asked.

"Oh, Di," I said, shaking my head in surrender. "Who knows what he is up to now?"

When Nicky returned, he unloaded the last of the boxes, then covered all the windows by taping newspapers on the inside, then double–padlocked the door, saying he would call me tomorrow. Which, of course, meant absolutely nothing.

Surprisingly though, he did call the next day making small talk. "How are you? How are the kids? How many seizures did Katy have?" And he called every day that whole week, never mentioning the garage and its contents. It felt good hearing his voice so often, so I pretended he really cared, even though I knew he was just checking to see if I had any information for him. But soon, Nicky's calls came to a halt and I didn't hear from him the entire next week.

Diane stood at my front door, calling me with an urgency in her voice.

"Sami. Quick. Let me in."

"Hi, Di. What's going on?" I asked, unlatching the screen.

"You're being watched. I'm sure of it. I saw a dark blue car parked down the street last night with two guys in it and when I got up this morning they were still there in the same place. I'm worried for you, Sami; you could be arrested for receiving stolen goods."

For the next forty-eight hours, the blue car remained in close proximity to our house. When I wasn't home, Diane observed it circling around the block, then returning to the same lookout point. Finally, on Friday, I got a call from Nicky.

"Hey, Sami, how you doin'?"

"What do you mean, 'How am I doing?' I'm being watched twenty-four hours a day. How do you think I'm doing? What in the hell are you hiding in the garage?"

"What makes you think you're being watched?"

"Diane spotted two guys parked down the street in a dark blue car. They circle the house when I leave and they're there day and night. I'm telling you, the cops are staking us out."

"The two of you are delusional. There's no one watching you. Don't be ridiculous."

"Where are you, Nicky, and when are you coming to get this stuff out of our garage?"

"I'm in L.A. doing a favor for Carlo. You hang tight and, just in case, remember, if they are cops, they can't search the house without a warrant. Always ask for a warrant. You got that? I'll be in touch."

Nicky flew home from L.A. the next night. Sneaking through the back alley, then creeping through the backyard, he knocked so softly I could barely hear him.

"Turn out the lights," he commanded, ducking down. He looked white as ghost.

"You're right," he said. "I just checked it out and we are being watched. Have you heard the news yet?" he asked.

"What news?" I asked.

"They got Johnny. He's dead," and tears pooled in his eyes. Sickened by his own words, Nicky couldn't speak. He reached for me and wrapped my hands in his. We sat silent for a few minutes.

"What now, Nicky?" I asked.

"I don't know. I'll keep in touch. I have to get out of here." He crept out the back door as quietly as he had slipped in.

The shocking morning headlines and the gruesome article made me tear up.

**NORTH SABLE MOBSTER,
JOHNNY BORONO, FOUND DEAD**

Johnny had stepped out onto the front porch to get the morning paper and his head had been blown off; it had landed thirty feet away from his body on the front lawn. His poor wife had run outside after hearing the shots and had followed the trail of bloody pieces of brain to his head, with half his face missing and one bulging eye staring up at her. Her harrowing screams woke the entire neighborhood.

That same day, two FBI agents knocked on my door. They were very polite and introduced themselves.

"Good morning, I am Agent Ralph Polanski, and this is my partner agent, Cliff Porter. We are from the FBI," he said flashing his credentials. "We would like to come in and ask you a few questions."

"Of course," I said, trying to smooth out the shakiness in my voice. "Come in."

I led them to the kitchen table and asked them to have a seat. Katy sat in the midst of her daily ritual of touching the Ohs to her head and throwing them on the table, then repeating, "chee chee," as I had forgotten to give her the cheese. My other kids were curious and pulled away from the TV to peek in and say hi, then went into show-off mode and performed the normal circus routine: jumping, giggling, and singing along with the TV, "Can you tell me how to get, how to get to Sesame Street?"

"Would either of you like a cup of coffee? I just made it."

Both agents watched as I handed Katy her "chee," which she promptly threw across the table, almost landing in Agent Polanski's lap. The agents glanced at one another. I thought I noted a tone of sympathy in Agent Polanski's voice.

"No, thank you. We just had coffee. We're fine."

I poured myself a cup of coffee and sat at the table next to Katy.

"Okay, Mrs. Salatto, where is he?" Agent Polanski asked.

"You mean Nicky. How would I know? We're separated."

"Can we search the house?"

Shaken, I could barely force the words out of my mouth.

"Do you have a search warrant?

"No. As a matter of fact, we don't, but we can get one."

"Yes, well… I need a warrant," I repeated dutifully.

Agent Polanski made a call for the warrant while I tried to busy myself coaxing Katy to drink her milk, trying not to act nervous. Without warning, Katy's head fell back. Her arm jerked out of control, forcing the glass out of my hand. The milk flew across the table and onto the floor amid the splintered glass. I kept Katy from falling out of her chair and Agent Porter jumped up to help me. With the aid of the other agent, Agent Porter lifted Katy to the floor then turned her on her side. As soon as I knew they had her, I moved to the sink and held onto the counter, staring out the window at that damn garage and feeling every fiber in my body begin to shake.

"What do I do? Shall I call an ambulance?" Agent Polanski asked nervously.

"No, it isn't necessary," I said softly, barely able to force the air through my vocal chords. "She'll come out of the seizure on her own. Just hold her for me… hold her."

There was never a good time for Katy to have a seizure, but if there had been, that would have been the perfect moment. Not only did I have the support of two capable people right in the same room but I felt they were suddenly on my side. Poor Katy pulled out of the seizure, and with the help of the two agents she sat back in her chair saying, "chee" like nothing had happened. I cleaned up the mess from the milk spill, then sipped my lukewarm coffee.

Agents Porter and Polanski remained at the house until the twenty other agents pulled up in ten cars outside. I'm sure the whole neighborhood must have been buzzing with curiosity. The agents began to tear the house apart while Agent Porter and I took the kids to the backyard to play. The children stood with worried faces, looking back at their home, concerned and confused.

"It's okay, kids," I assured them. "These men are searching for evidence that may have been left by the last homeowners. You know, the people who lived here before we did." Agent Porter kindly confirmed my fib.

"Your mother is right. There is no need to be worried. We will be out of here in no time. Now who is going to play catch?"

My children rebounded with enthusiasm. They were willing to trust so easily and, starved for male attention. I nodded and smiled at Agent Porter and basked in the feeling of comfort and support I had never felt from my own husband.

It didn't take long for the kids to get hungry and, of course, there was no way to go back in and fix lunch. Agent Polanski said, "Who wants to go to McDonald's?"

The jumping and screaming of "Yes, yes, yes," from my kids brought the only uplifting moment of the day. Agents Ralph Polanski and Cliff Porter drove us all to McDonald's and bought our lunch, and even paid for it. By the time we returned from lunch, the garage, with its broken padlocks, stood empty, paper torn from the windows and the last of its contents, $200,000 worth of cashmere sweaters, loaded on a large truck.

As we went inside, Cliff Porter apologized for the cyclone that had passed through our home and even helped me push some of the heavier pieces of furniture back in place.

"Are you going to arrest me?" I asked them, tears filling my eyes.

"No, Sami. We've been watching you for some time now," said Agent Polanski, "and we know you didn't have anything to do with this crime. I will warn you, though, we won't look the other way if your husband ever places you in this position again."

The next morning, I got a call from Agent Porter telling me that Nicky had just been arrested, after a high-speed chase on Highway 47, with a bag full of money and a gun on the front seat of his car. He was charged with a federal offence.

I hung up the phone, trying to form the explanation in my head that I now had to tell my children, and could hardly catch my breath between sobs.

- The Ladies -

Texting Saturday Evening, 11:30 p.m.

Lena, I think I've got the book title.
How about The Godmother?
You know, like The Godfather?

Sami, you're not a godmother.
That's ridiculous.

I am too a godmother.
I've baptized two kids.

Yes, but you're not "that kind"
of godmother. Are you drinking, Sami?

Well, yes, just a little tequila. However,
I still think it's worth pondering.

Okay, ponder away.
It's your story and I'll title it whatever you like.
But I still think it's ridiculous.

Don't get snippy.
I'm just brain-farting.

I think you mean brainstorming.
No, on second thought,
I think brain-farting describes it best.

Ha-ha. Good night, cousin.

Good night, Sami.

- Chapter 14 -
Bail and Bonds

Nicky was out on bail faster than an Italian can slip in, come, and slip out. He even made it out in time to go to Johnny's funeral. Johnny's coffin, blanketed with carnations, roses, and lilies, sat in the spotlight encircled by the familiar Italian faces seen at my wedding, church feasts, and Sunday masses. Only now, everyone looked much older and sadder. His mother's sobs floated over the "*Ave Maria.*" Diane and I were standing together at the gravesite when Nicky arrived late, as usual, with Carlo and his brother Norm in their black Cadillac.

Diane spotted them first and dug her elbow in my side, nodding her head toward their opened car door. Out stepped the three of them dressed in black overcoats, black suits, and black hats. They walked through the cemetery, stepping over graves toward the funeral crowd three abreast. Diane leaned into me and softly whispered, "Would you just look at that? Are we at a funeral or watching a scene from a mafia movie?" Nicky nodded at me over the casket and disappeared before it was lowered.

I had refused Nicky's plea to put our house up as collateral to make bail, thus, "the wop greeting." At least the kids and I had warmth and shelter and there was no way I would jeopardize that. I'm sure Carlo put up Nicky's bail. I mean, who else would be dumb enough to trust him? Besides, Carlo had Nicky by the balls and he knew it.

It took two years before Nicky came to trial and while he was out on bond he continued to pull jobs for the mafia. He sold stolen loads of chickens, cigarettes, and Beefeater Gin; the gin heist led him to Vegas and his fourth arrest. All the while Carlo Russo posted bond after bond, rolling them out as fast as a newspaper is printed. Nicky did give me some money during this time and I'm sure it was dirty. But I was desperate to make ends meet. He also slept with me once in a while. Nothing compared to being held in the arms of the man I loved. Like the old song goes, "For whatever my man is, I am his forever more." Plus, it gave the kids a chance to see him too. I actually hoped he would have to serve time. Thought maybe it would straighten him out. I still loved him, and I hoped, in his own way, he loved me too.

Agents Cliff Porter and Ralph Polanski continued to trail me around like bloodhounds. I got so that I felt secure knowing that they were watching me. I had my own private security guards. It felt so presidential and we were on a first name basis. Usually when I arrived home after dark, I'd look over my shoulder to see their car slowly pass my house. I'd wave and smile and usually Cliff would roll the window down and say, "Good night, Sami."

When Nicky finally went to trial, he would glance at me sitting in the courtroom and give me the Italian head nod hello and sometimes a wink. Any sign of affection left me loving him even more. I didn't miss a day of the proceedings and I know Nicky appreciated it. He made handcuffs look like a fashion statement. He was still the most handsome man I'd ever seen. The jury found him guilty and his attorneys immediately filed an appeal. I have no idea who was pulling whose strings but Nicky still was not incarcerated. That night Nicky made love to me with a tenderness I'd never known from him.

Two weeks later my phone rang. Nicky's voice sounded hopeless. "I have to be at the federal building tomorrow at 8:00 a.m. and was told not to drive myself. Can you take me, Sami? My dad won't."

On the drive down the next morning, Nicky grabbed my hand and I could feel his shaking. We didn't talk much, too scared because we both suspected that today would be the end of the ride. Once we were inside the federal building, his suited escorts led him through a heavy gray door that slammed shut, the sound echoing through the halls. I sat waiting for an hour until I was told to leave. He wasn't coming out.

For three weeks, I went crazy trying to find out where they took him and could not get any answers. I told our kids as simply as I could, "Daddy took some things that didn't belong to him. You know that stealing is a sin, but it is also against the law and now Daddy has to be punished. He is in prison. But he told me to tell you that he loves you."

Their innocent eyes glistened as we wrapped ourselves in a family hug.

The next night I waved Agent Porter over as he drove by the house.

"Cliff, how do I find out where they sent Nicky? I can't get any information and I'm going crazy."

Shaking his head, Cliff asked, "You really care about this guy after how he put you at risk?"

Tears spilled onto my cheeks. "He is the father of my kids and he's still my husband."

"Well, he won't be playing either one of those roles for a while," he said, as he handed me his handkerchief.

"Okay, my guess is, he was probably sent for processing to the La Tuna Federal Penitentiary, about 18 miles north of El Paso in the middle of the desert. You'll be getting some information soon."

My silence hung heavy in the air and punctuated the reality that Nicky was truly gone, and now, for sure… I was alone.

"You know, Sami," Cliff said, "you're a beautiful woman and you shouldn't shed any more tears or spend any more time on a man who doesn't deserve you." His kind words moved me. I touched Cliff's cheek softly saying, "Thank you, Agent Porter. You have been more than kind."

I turned my back to him, went inside, and leaned my back against the closed door, listening. It took about thirty seconds before I heard Porter's footsteps slowly walk away.

- Chapter 15 -
The Visit

After Nicky was put away, I needed a job desperately and Carlo provided it—waitressing in his restaurant, Luigi's—which turned out to be my lifeline. The job was both a blessing and a curse. Carlo hung out there a lot. Whenever he arrived, no matter what song played on the jukebox, Carlo gave back the customer's quarters, then pumped dozens of coins into the box and punched the button to play the only song he would allow in the restaurant when he was there: "*On the Sunny Side of the Street.*" Over and over and over, it played until most everyone took a cue from the lyrics… "Grab your coat and get your hat, leave your worry on the doorstep. Just direct your feet…" as far away from this restaurant as possible! It hurt my tips from the regular customers because they could only take so much of that song, no matter how good the Italian food. But the restaurant served as a drawing card for all the hoods in town who usually carried a lot of cash and Carlo made sure they tipped me well.

"How did you do tonight, sweetie?" Carlo asked every night, coming up behind me, slipping his arm around my waist, his chin on my shoulder, his eyes on my cleavage as I counted my tips. Thank God for his brother, Norm, who would pull him away saying, "Come on, leave her alone, she's a married woman," and he'd get him off of me. The cat-and-mouse game with Carlo went on the whole time I worked there, but the job paid the bills and if it hadn't been for Carlo, I wouldn't have been able to make that first trip to see Nicky.

Agent Porter was right. I finally heard from the prison. I could write Nicky anytime and telephone, as long as I accepted all charges. Each letter and call left me elated. I felt he really loved me for the very first time. I know it sounds kind of crazy, but I still keep the love letters he wrote to me while incarcerated. This was his first:

Dear Sami,

I can't tell you how much I miss you and the kids. Being here is a real wake-up call and made me realize how much I have screwed up my life and yours too, I guess. Thank you for being at the trial. I loved looking back in the court room and seeing your beautiful eyes. I lay in my bunk and visualize the last time we made love. It makes me horny as hell, so that is frustrating, but I do it anyway. Believe me, when I get out of here things are going to be different. We will be a real family and we're going to find a cure for Katy. I miss you and the kids. Tell them I love them. I love you too, beautiful.

Nicky

P.S. If you have a minute, I could use some cigarettes. Marlboro is what most everyone of the guys smoke down here and it sure can get you some favors when you need them. Thanks.

I soaked in those letters, all forty-seven of them, like a parched flower struggling to bloom in the desert. I felt my prayers had finally been answered: he loves me. After a time, I began to notice there was always a "P.S." at the end of his letters.

P.S. I could sure use some new underwear.
P.S. If you can, I need a few extra bucks.
P.S. I've been moved to the minimum security and given the job of cutting the golf greens. They said I could play a round of golf when my work is done. See if you can pick up some clubs for me. Thanks babe.

I knew I was Nicky's key to the outside world, so he had to keep me happy, but maybe, just maybe, some of it was true, and he did love me. I desperately needed to believe that. I tore open every letter the minute it arrived. Even our mailman noticed my anticipation and would ring the doorbell, wave the letter through the window saying, "You got one, Sami." I dutifully followed through on every one of Nicky's P.S. requests.

While Nicky was still serving time in La Tuna, his other offenses came up and he would have to be transferred back home for trial. This required an escort by a U.S. marshal. Coincidentally, the marshal turned out to be an old neighbor and boyhood friend of Nicky's named Tom Largo. Tom was assigned to transfer Nicky via car and asked if I would like to ride down there with him and his wife. We could pick up Nicky, then the four of us could take our time, spend one overnight, have a few nice meals before arriving back in Sable. Nicky and I were thrilled, so I arranged for Diane to watch the kids.

The day we were to leave, Tom phoned saying something had come up for his wife and she wouldn't be able to come with us. Would I still be interested in driving with him? Shocked but not surprised, I listened to his seedy proposition,

"Of course, you know, we might have to share a room on the way down, but I'm sure you won't mind, because you'll get to be with Nicky on the way back. Right?" he asked.

"No, Tom, it's not alright." I said, disgusted. "If your wife is not coming, perhaps we should fly down there. Or… I could call your office and ask your superior what he suggests. Right?"

My threat worked, and Tom made our reservations to fly out the next day. Carlo happily paid all my expenses to keep Nicky happy, so he wouldn't testify against him.

After arriving we went to a hotel and I was told to wait in the lobby while Tom picked up Nicky. I chose a large chair facing the door, so I could watch Nicky walk through. I could hardly sit still; crossing and uncrossing my legs, tapping my fingers, standing to circle the chair then sitting again, filled with anticipation.

Then the strangest thing happened. The door to the lobby opened and in walked Steve McQueen and Ali MacGraw. He walked past me and said, "How you doing today?"

Needless to say, I was taken aback but I managed to say, "Fine. How are you?"

"We are terrific," he said, "and this is the best ice cream in town." He held a dripping double-deck strawberry cone out for me to take a lick. I was too stunned to find my own tongue and Ali MacGraw doubled over with laughter at what must have been the sight of my eyes bulging like golf balls out of my head and my mouth hanging open. At that moment, Tom and Nicky walked through the door and Nicky greeted Steve McQueen like an old buddy. Steve slapped him on the back and Nicky introduced me.

"Steve, this is my wife, Sami, that I told you about."

"Is this guy your husband?" Steve asked me jokingly. "He's good-looking enough to be a movie star. You got to get him out of prison," he said laughing as he told us to have a great visit and disappeared into the hotel dining room.

Nicky's face turned red and he gave me a big bear hug as I asked, "What was that all about?" Nicky explained that a movie was being shot called *The Getaway*, a Sam Peckinpah film, and many of the scenes were in and around the prison, using the actual inmates as extras. McQueen and one hundred and thirty crew members were scheduled to film inside the wall. They were warned by the prison officials that if a hostage situation occurred with anyone working on the film, including Steve McQueen, they would not be responsible, they "would not negotiate with inmates, they'd shoot first and ask questions later." After meeting Nicky on the inside, half joking, half not, McQueen asked him to watch his back and Nicky took the task seriously. Consequently, Nicky was sitting next to McQueen when the camera panned in for a close-up. They got to talking during a break from filming and Nicky told him about me and our upcoming visit. I've seen that movie dozens of times just for the two-second shot of Nicky shoulder to shoulder with Steve McQueen.

That evening, Tom took us to dinner in Juarez. The excitement and risk of crossing the border with an incarcerated convict in the car only heightened the romance of that night. We drank, danced, and partied, then returned to the hotel and made love for hours. After all, it had been nine long months.

The following morning, we boarded the plane back to Sable. On arrival, Tom allowed us a few moments to say goodbye; Nicky kissed me like it was our last. My heart ached when Tom apologized as he handcuffed Nicky and took him away.

- The Ladies -

Mid-Morning Email, 11 a.m.

To: Sami@hotmail
From: Lena@gmail
Subject: Won't be writing for a while

Hi Sami,

I have a small issue. It seems I'm going to need a knee replacement. Damn! On the upside, if they keep taking small parts of me away, POOF! I'll just disappear and save the cost of a burial.

No worries though. I plan to get back to the book as soon as possible. Who knows, maybe I'll be able to devote more time to writing while I am recouping. I'll let you know more details when I get them. Love you.

Lena

To: Lena@gmail
From: Sami@hotmail
Subject: Health Alert

Oh honey, I'm so sorry to hear this. You take care of yourself. We have plenty of time to write this book. Well...I guess that isn't true, is it? Either one of us could pass away at any moment now (I know, you keep me around for the laughs). I think I read somewhere that Stephen King said that one should be able to write a book in three months. If Stephen says it can be done, we shall do it. I think we both have at least three good months left, don't you? Sending a big hug.

- *Chapter 16* -

The Day The Music Died

After Johnny's murder, the mood at Luigi's restaurant took a serious dive and the jukebox stood eerily silent. Carlo dressed immaculately in his Italian silk suit—signature unlit Cuban cigar hanging from his mouth—sat on his corner barstool, farthest away from the door, staring at the shot of whiskey in front of him.

Two huge Italian men, Sal and Big Bobby, guarded the restaurant. I called them the "collection crew" because they would go after the deadbeats who owed Carlo money. Sal was 300 pounds and over six feet; Bobby was as wide as he was tall, stocky, and looked like a human bulldozer. His looks alone would prompt one to empty wallets and pockets.

Carlo's men called me "Nicky's wife," never by my name. Sal would say, "How's Nicky's wife doing tonight, huh?" Or, "Hey Nicky's wife, bring me a cup of coffee, will you, babe?" They even called me "Nicky's wife" when they were coming on to me. "Nicky's wife is looking pretty sexy tonight. Come and give your big teddy bear a hug, will you?"

On slow nights Bobby loved to tell and retell the story

of his wedding night because, he said, "My honeymoon night was proof that my marriage would last. See, the night me and my wife got married, we stayed at the Sable Continental Hotel where we had our reception. After we went to our room, and, you know, did our thing and fell asleep, the damn phone rings and it's the boss. He wanted me to take care of something right then, and it's two in the morning. So, I get dressed and tell my wife that I have to go somewhere. She said, "Okay," turned over and went back to sleep. No kidding, not one question, not even when I got back at 7:00 a.m. I knew right then and there that I married the right dame."

The phone on the wall behind the bar went unanswered for five rings, so I interrupted Bobby and ran to pick it up.

"Luigi's, this is Sami. How can I help you?"

"Is Carlo there?" the gruff voice on the other side inquired.

"Who's calling, please?" I asked, afraid to divulge Carlo's actual whereabouts.

"It's Joe Bonanno, I'm returning his call," the impatient voice said.

My heart skipped a beat but I managed a "Just a minute please," then rushed over to Carlo at the end of the bar and whispered in his ear.

"I'll take it in the back room," Carlo said. "Just hang on till I pick up." I returned to the phone and held it to my ear until I heard Carlo's voice saying, "Joe, thanks for calling back. Hang up now, Sami," Carlo ordered.

I pressed the receiver down, glanced around the room to see if anyone was watching. Then curiosity—yeah, the one that did in the cat—urged me to lift my finger up ever so easily. I heard Carlo say he needed a favor, and a shudder went through my entire body when I heard the request and Bonanno's response confirming, "I'll contact a guy to take care of it." I pressed the button down softly and replaced the phone in the cradle as if it were a sleeping baby, when a familiar voice behind me made me jump.

"Hi, Sami," he said. It was Agent Cliff Porter. I whipped around like a kid who just got caught with a finger in the frosting.

"You look like you just saw a ghost. Hope it wasn't bad news," he said.

"Oh hi, Cliff. Oh, no just a customer," I said, trying to sound casual. "How are you?"

"I'm hungry. Any good specials tonight?" he inquired.

"The lasagna is outstanding."

"I'll have it and a coke with no ice," he requested.

Cliff ate quickly, handing me a more than generous tip on his way out the door.

"You working late tonight?" he asked.

"No. It's slow, so I should be off within a half hour."

"See you then," Cliff said, smiling.

After Nicky was locked up, Cliff took it upon himself to look out for me and would drive by my house about the time I usually got off work. He sat in his car in the usual place, across the street and two houses down from mine. Still feeling nervous about the conversation,

I overheard, I motioned for him to come closer. He pulled up in front of the house. His handsome face, blond hair and hazel eyes glowed under the street lamp as he leaned over the passenger side and rolled down the window.

"What's up, Sami? You want to talk?"

"Yes, Cliff. I do. Can you come inside for a minute?" I asked.

After entering, he accidentally slammed the door hard enough to rattle the windows. Wincing, he said, "Oh shit. God, I'm so sorry. Will that wake the kids?"

"No, Cliff. Tina is spending the night at her friend's and the other three are with their grandmother. I think I need a drink. How about you?"

"No, thanks. I'm still on duty."

I poured myself a double gin on the rocks, a nightly habit I got into since Nicky's incarceration two years before. We settled on the couch, and after a few sips I began to feel the calming effect of the liquor.

"How are Katy's seizures?" he asked.

"I guess better, but still happening and she is higher than a kite on meds."

Cliff was such a thoughtful guy, strong and reliable. Having him follow me around was comforting. I wished that Nicky could be as caring. My guts were screaming at me to tell Cliff what I heard on Carlo's call; that's why I invited him in in the first place. Instead, I froze in fear for my life and my children's safety if I was ever found out. Another double gin helped to drown the horrible secret and made me less afraid. I'm not sure if it was the booze, or the months of loneliness, but I reached over and touched Cliff's hand and he responded by gently holding mine. Tears spilled onto my cheeks and he wiped them away, then, turned my head toward his and kissed my forehead. I melted into his chest and he held me for a long while.

"Thank you, Cliff. I'm feeling pretty vulnerable tonight. I better get to bed. I have a busy day tomorrow," I said, getting up and trying to pull out of my stupor.

"You don't have to thank me," he said, staring into my eyes. Cliff got up and slowly walked toward the door, placing his hand on the knob. I quickly put my hand on top of his.

"Can you stay, please?" I asked, hesitantly, uncertain of what I was about to do. His answer came in the urgent way he pulled me toward him and pressed his lips hard on mine.

One week later, the ice cream parlor on Faro Street that served as a front for a gambling operation run by an opposing mob family exploded into millions of pieces, widowing three more North Sable wives. One of their husbands was responsible for Johnny Borono's death. There isn't a day that goes by that I haven't regretted eavesdropping on that telephone conversation. You can't imagine the burden of carrying around a secret of that magnitude all of your life. The killer responsible for that hit is still alive and kicking today.

- Chapter 17 -

The Unlucky Wives Club

After two years, Nicky finished his federal sentence and got transferred back to Sable to face state charges, including burglary, drugs, and gun possession. Three other mobsters were involved in the same crime and all four of them were being tried together. The state didn't have a strong case against Nicky but for the testimony of one guy, Rick Vitola. If Rick didn't implicate the other three men, including Nicky, he would be the only one to serve any time.

I attended the two-week trial. For the first twelve days, Rick repeated over and over, "I respectfully refuse to answer," whenever the prosecuting attorney referred to Nicky and the other two men. On every break, he assured us he wasn't going to rat on anyone. There was a good chance Nicky would get off if Rick kept his mouth shut. In court, I sat with the other wives of the accused men. We formed a bond and jokingly called ourselves "The Unlucky Wives Club."

On the thirteenth day of trial, Rick appeared with dark circles under his eyes and looked as though he hadn't slept all night, which was the case. The authorities got to him, somehow. As he walked into the courtroom, his eyes never left the floor, wouldn't look at any of us. Then he sang like a bird. He even made the courtroom laugh at Nicky's expense when he testified that "Nicky would get so nervous every time we pulled a job that we had to plan pit stops to keep him from crapping his pants."

No surprise when the jury foreman announced, "Guilty." The seven-year additional sentence left my eyes locked with Nicky's as they handcuffed him and took him away, again.

When I look back, I can't believe what a circus surrounded us. On more than one occasion, instead of watching Saturday morning cartoons, my kids peered through our front window to watch the cops chase the bookie that lived across the street. He would burst out the front door in his pajamas and bare feet, holding the phone which he had torn out of his wall, then he would attempt to outrun the police.

On weekends we visited Nicky at the Logan prison. I know, not your average family outing. I would pack a lunch of sausage and pepper sandwiches, cookies, fresh fruit, plus whatever weekly request that Nicky had made. The two-hour ride to the prison with the kids became a weekly trek. The Unlucky Wives Club would take turns meeting at each of our houses, then caravan down to see our husbands.

On the drive down, we played I Spy or sang "*99 Bottles of Beer*" and attempted to get every trucker that we passed to honk his horn. Believe me, the drive to the prison was a fun family time and Nicky came to expect our visit with no consideration of my 6:00 p.m. to 2:00 a.m. work schedule. Our children became friends with the other prisoners' kids and loved getting together to play with them each week. Hey, it became routine and kids thrive on that.

Katy's needs made it too difficult to take her with us. Besides, Mama insisted on taking Katy full time after I told her what had happened to my youngest boy, Sonny. One day, during the trial, I got stuck in traffic and didn't make it home in time to get Katy off her bus from daycare. Sonny, (eleven at the time) got home from school and let himself in, then heard Katy's driver honking out front. He went out to get his sister off the bus. "Please give your mom this note from the nurse," the driver said, handing it to Sonny. Sonny unfolded the paper that explained Katy had been awfully quiet that afternoon. It warned to keep an eye on her because her silence usually preceded a seizure.

The note scared Sonny, so he placed his sister on the floor in the middle of our living room and surrounded her with her favorite stuffed toys just in case. When I arrived home, I found my sweet Sonny crying as he cradled Katy's head, as she was having a full-blown, grand mal seizure.

- The Ladies -
Evening Call 7 p.m.

Just a hair past eight o'clock Lena threw back another Toll House chocolate chip morsel from her ration which she strategically placed in a delicate English cup and saucer—hand painted with yellow, blue and purple flowers. She attempted to tame her addiction to the tiny chocolate bits by sucking on them one at time, rather than chewing, to make them last longer.

Lena dialed Sami's number as she savored the very last chip in her allotment. When Sami answered the phone after the first ring (highly unusual), the shock caused Lena to inhale and she began choking on the small morsel. All Sami heard was her cousin gasping for air as she coughed for what seemed like an eternity.

Sami: Lena, Lena, shall I hang up and call 911?
Lena: *No, no, give me a minute.*

Her coughing and spurting continued until finally, she took a deep, difficult breath and began her sneezing ritual.

Three sneezes later:

Sami: What caused that?
Lena: *One of those tiny chips used in cookies. I suck on them when I'm writing. Did you know that in Holland and Sweden they give children chocolate for breakfast every morning and they have some of the happiest, healthiest kids on Earth?*
Sami: What does that have to do with you, honey?
Lena: *Well, I want to be happy while I'm writing. Of course, there's the reverse effect when I get on the scale; But vanity should really be phased out when you reach your seventies, don't you think? Hey, it's better than making the cookies. Just think of all the unhealthy ingredients I've eliminated: flour, butter, sugar. Agreed?*
Sami: Okay, whatever you say. Are you sure you're alright?
Lena: *I'm fine, just a little obsessed with your story.*
Sami: You are so funny. It makes me happy that you are so enthusiastic and involved in our project. What's on your mind?
Lena: *Well, when Rick implicated Nicky and the rest of the guys, what was in it for Rick?*
Sami: Rick got immunity and was placed in a witness protection program.
Lena: *Is he still around?*
Sami: Who knows? No one has seen or heard from him since. I've heard rumors that once in a while

he contacted his sister; but she died a few years ago, hopefully of natural causes; with the mob, you never know for sure. You know what I do know for sure?

Lena: *Pray tell!*

Sami: I'm thinking of getting extensions: hair and eyelashes. What do you think?

Lena: *I think I'm eating too much chocolate and you need to go read a good book on self-acceptance. Try The Self-Acceptance Process. I love you. Talk to you soon.*

Sami: But what…

Lena hung up, refusing to discuss Sami's search for the fountain of youth. She snatched one more chocolate morsel from the bag to make up for the mishap and returned to her writing.

- Chapter 18 -
The Fight

Funny, with Nicky serving time, our home became peaceful: no yelling, no fighting. It settled our kids down a bit, too. As strange as it may seem, the weekly routine of taking them to visit their father in prison forced us to be a family and have good times together for a change.

Before his incarceration, at the height of the mess we were in, Nicky and I had horrible fights. Unfortunately, some in front of the kids. My children still remind me of one in particular; they named it "the night of the spaghetti."

Nicky and the children were at the dinner table, eating salad, and I got up to start shoveling the pasta onto the plates, when out of Nicky's mouth came, "The salad has too much vinegar, as usual." Then "When are you going to learn not to burn the garlic bread?" He followed this with a remark to the kids, "One day your mom is going to learn to cook, right, kids?"

I had just dished up a huge plate of pasta for him and felt the anger coming to a boil inside me. I walked up behind him and dumped the whole thing (sauce and all) over his head. There followed a moment of shock. The kids' mouths dropped open, silence all around. Then he slowly rose from the table, turned toward me, noodles draped over his head and shoulders, sauce dripping over his face, down his back and I burst into laughter and so did the kids. But the sudden slap across my face stopped all the giggling and I almost fell from the force. I turned into a wild animal, rushed at him, pushed his hands aside and managed to get close enough to bite him on his forehead. He screamed in pain and the whole scene came to a halt.

"You're a crazy woman. You know that, Sami?" he yelled, holding his bleeding head as he started toward the bathroom.

"You're the one who made me that way, Nicky," I screamed back at him.

After he doctored his wound, showered, and changed clothes, he walked out the door and I didn't see him for four days. He wore my bite marks on his head for two weeks.

"Who bit you on the head?" his buddies asked.

"My crazy wife. She's like a bomb that goes off when you least expect it."

He used the scar as proof to blame me for all the dysfunction in our relationship.

That was the first time I actually had the guts to stand up to his bullying. Now I knew I had the strength to hurt him, too. I cleaned the red strands off the chair and floor, smiling the whole time. The mess was so worth it!

Years later, while Nicky was still serving time, we

laughed about that fight. Nicky kept being moved from the high security sections of the prison to the lower security sections because of his "good behavior." Finally, just before he was released, he was sent to a halfway house. He phoned me on my night off and asked what I was doing, and could I get a sitter and come over for a late-night quickie? Thank God for Diane. She was always there for me.

I was to drive past the place and go to the back. If the light was on, I should just keep driving because that meant the guard was near. If it was off, I was to kill my car lights and turn into the back entrance. Sort of a "one if by land, two if by sea" scenario.

The light was off and I did as I was told. Nicky stuck his head out the door and motioned for me to run in. He led me straight to a broom closet. The tight quarters made it difficult to make love; but we did, fast and furious. After, I looked up into his eyes and smiled.

"Who gave you that nasty scar on your forehead?" I teased him.

"Some crazy broad I used to know," he said laughing. "And she ruined a perfectly good silk shirt of mine, too. I'm pretty sure she was a vampire because she sure liked to draw blood."

- Chapter 19 -

Released

"Okay, babe, it's over. I'm free. Please come get me." Finally, Nicky won probation and his voice trembled when he phoned.

We only had two hours' warning. The kids and I rushed through the house like a tornado, sucking up anything that was out of place. I made a chocolate box cake and popped it into the oven, then showered and washed my hair. I put on my makeup as carefully as I did on my wedding day almost 13 years earlier and picked out black pants and a light green blouse, cut low enough to reveal my cleavage. I gave the kids an art project to make a **WELCOME HOME DADDY** sign, then left Tina, now twelve years old, in charge of frosting the cake and watching her siblings.

When I drove up to the halfway house, Nicky stood outside holding an envelope with his personal items, including every letter I'd ever sent to him in one hand and a plastic bag with his clothes in the other.

I got out of the car and we walked slowly toward each other, smiling. He dropped his belongings and wrapped his arms around me, our tears mingled, and we didn't let go for several minutes. He looked into my eyes, and I felt in that moment… Nicky loved me. He flashed that gorgeous smile and said, "You know, we have to stop meeting like this. Let's go home, baby."

By the time we arrived at the house, the welcome sign was hung in the window and the kids were waiting on the front lawn, jumping up and down, yelling, "Daddy, Daddy," as our car approached.

The children called Mama to tell her the news, so she arrived with a pan of her homemade lasagna and Katy in tow. The celebration went on the rest of the day. Donny and Sonny were elated to have the attention of their dad, who played catch with them for two hours, then sat with Tina to go over her school project, titled "Living Without a Dad." It included a collage of all the photos we had taken at the prison and a heartbreaking essay that detailed the void she had felt for all those years. After reading it, Nicky put his arms around her and we cried for the second time that day. He attempted to connect with Katy, too, but she wouldn't acknowledge him, and you could see the hurt expression fall over his face. Katy never did let too many people get close.

The first family dinner in many years began with a toast by Nicky. "I've dreamt about this day for a long time and I want to thank you all for standing by me. I apologize for the hurt my actions caused. So, this is to my mother-in-law, Saint Maria, who watches over our Katy tirelessly, to the greatest children, and the best wife a man can have." I'll never forget the magic of that day, a new beginning for us all.

The very next weekend, we were invited to a welcome home party given by several of our friends. I pretended to listen to the woman standing in front of me talking a mile a minute about God knows what, as I strained to eavesdrop on the conversation between Nicky and another friend. He told him how grateful he was that I stood by him and how he would make it all up to me.

I truly believed he meant it, but the reality of life for a convicted felon set in fast and the magic disappeared as quickly as a rabbit into a top hat. Nicky applied for job after job, with no results. Discouraged after five months, he spent a lot of time at Carlo's, drinking with the old crowd. Familiar patterns set in and we began to argue again. I grew more suspicious as he came home later and later each night and asked Di if she would come with me to spy on him. We followed him to a popular night club and waited for half an hour before going in. He remained calm on the dance floor when I pulled him away from the young girl he was kissing.

"Is this how you make things up to me Nicky?" I said, angry and crying.

"What you see is what you get, Sami," he said slurring his words, pulling the young girl back into his arms. He didn't even attempt to defend his actions and my eyes confirmed what I had suspected all along.

There were so many reasons to kick Nicky out of my life but seeing him in the arms of someone else was the turning point for me. I knew all along he had been unfaithful, but to actually see his tongue in her mouth killed something inside of me. Suddenly a clarity came over me. Nicky arrived home two days later to a pile of his clothes and belongings on the front lawn and the door locks changed. He threw down the useless key then kicked the front door and cursed me as he loaded his stuff in his car. I started divorce proceedings immediately—I began the long process of releasing Nicky Salatto from my life, finally and forever.

Living Without A Dad

By

Tina Salatto

I'm going to tell you something you may not know, because I try not to tell anyone where my father is. He is in prison and I feel ashamed to share that unless I absolutely have to. He stole some stuff and got caught and Mom says now he has to pay.

I love him but sometimes I think I just love the idea of him. When I see a real family at the park, or at a school function I feel envious and sad. I want to be a part of a whole family.

Mom is so busy working and trying to take care of my sick sister that she barely has time for me or my brothers. They don't have anyone to teach them basketball or baseball and I missed the school "Dad Daughter Dance," which made me so sad that I cried myself to sleep. Sometimes, at night I don't feel safe in our house and I never felt that way when dad was home.

I guess the only good thing about Dad being gone is... Mom and Dad can't fight anymore.

But I would be willing to even put up with that if we could all go out to a movie or on a picnic together.

I hope he gets out before the next Dad Daughter Dance, if there is one. Also, maybe Mom and Dad won't fight anymore after they have had this long break. Sometimes, taking a break is all you need. When he gets out of jail, maybe we can all just love one another. That's what I really wish.

Please don't share this with the class or anyone else. Thank you.

- The Ladies -

Early Afternoon Call, 2 p.m.

Sami: I was cleaning out my closet and way in the back corner I found an old box filled with things my kids made when they were younger. You know cards, art work, reports. I found myself both laughing and crying as I looked through them.

Lena: *Is there anything we can use in the book?*

Sami: Yeah, I think so. There's a cartoon drawing that Donny made—I'm guessing—he must have been eight or nine at the time, of a man running down the street, holding a telephone, with a string of cops chasing him. It's funny, but sad; my kids had to witness awful things like that. Sonny drew a picture of the family holding hands with our names under each of the stick figures. The figure of "Daddy" was not connected with the rest of us; looked as though he was falling because he was upside down. Pitiful.

Lena: *Well Sonny got that one right didn't he? Nothing you could have done about that, honey. So, don't be sad.*

Sami: Also found a report that Tina wrote for a school paper titled "Living Without a Dad." To hear

how much she suffered in her own words… well, haven't been able to stop crying.
Lena: *Honey, you just get it all out. It's probably healthy. Remember, Sami, it wasn't your fault.*
Sami: Thanks Lena, I really needed to hear that. I love you. I'll call you soon.

- Chapter 20 -
Survival

After I kicked Nicky out of the house, I felt more depressed than ever. I think I had to struggle through my anxiety attacks (over Katy and the loss of Nicky) so intensely it activated a drive in me. With no hope of Nicky ever being financially responsible for our family, I went into survival mode with the force of a hurricane. There was nothing or no one who could put me down or stop the forward momentum. Deep down, I knew I would find a way to protect my kids and get out of the financial mess in which Nicky left us.

Then the solution came to me: cream puffs. I loved baking and cooking and everyone loved to eat my food, so I knew I had a good product. By day, I baked cream puffs; big, fluffy cream puffs with custard filling and Mama's chocolate frosting, and by night, I waitressed at a new hotel, The Crystal House, that opened in North Sable. Most people thought I was nuts. "You mean you work all night and go home after work and make cream puffs?" they would ask. Exactly! My cream puffs became a favorite dessert everywhere I sold them. This allowed me to be at home during the day if the kids needed me and offered another way to make ends meet.

I got home around 3:00 a.m., exhausted by the end of my night shift, but began the prep for the cream puffs in spite of it, slept between three and four hours, got up the next day and started baking. Some days, Tina, and Mama would help. We had an assembly line: I prepared the pastry, Mama made the custard, Tina filled and frosted. Katy sat watching and cheering us on with an occasional, "Dare," when we finished filling a tray.

Every once in a while, we would catch sight of one another with flour on our faces, telltale traces of chocolate frosting in the corners of our mouths (well, there had to be some pleasure amidst the pain) and drops of vanilla custard smearing our aprons, and we would crack up. I loaded the trays of cream puffs into my car and sold them to local restaurants, coffee shops, and convenience stores. Like a madwoman, I drove around town and sold out the batch before going to work by 6:00 p.m. each night. I still have nightmares that I'm trapped inside a giant cream puff, surrounded by custard pudding that slowly inches its way up to my nose.

When the cream puffs didn't bring in enough cash, I started making calzones, and eventually started a catering business specializing in Italian food. I prepared and delivered lunches for teachers' meetings and women's junior league groups, Sunday brunches at churches, and dinners for in-home private parties. I managed to keep my house, put food on the table, and clothes on our backs, but it almost sent me to an early grave. I did have help from Mama and Papa with the kids, and they loaned me money when I couldn't make ends meet, but even that wasn't enough to keep us afloat.

Desperate, I borrowed a credit card from my friend, Anna Lee, who worked with me at The Crystal House. Once a Playboy bunny, her dark hair, blue eyes, and six-foot frame always turned heads. She tried to date big, tall men because, she said, "I love it when a man folds his arms around me and makes me feel like a small pea." She knew how to handle the attention she got from men better than any woman I've ever known.

One night, an obnoxious businessman who had had too much to drink called Anna Lee over to his table.

"Hey beautiful," he said, slurring his words, "how much would it cost me to have you sit on my face?"

Without missing a beat, she quietly whispered in his ear, "Buddy, you couldn't even afford a sniff."

I kept Anna Lee's credit card for ten years and she never questioned me about it. I paid every bill on time, eventually paying the whole thing off and grew her credit line to $12,000; she was thrilled. She died from brain cancer at age forty-seven. I still miss her, and marvel at the trust she had in me.

- Chapter 21 -
The Crystal House

In the Crystal House Hotel, I worked in the lower-level dining room and nightclub called The Lion's Den. We wore short little outfits that resembled a lion tamer's costume with black, high-heeled boots. Only thing missing was a whip and chair, which would have actually come in handy at times, as the hotel brought in wealthy, drunk, businessmen on expense accounts.

The food, live entertainment, and dancing, made it a popular destination for the locals. Tips definitely improved, along with free access to alcohol. I soon learned, if you filled your time with too much to do and add a few drinks a day, the mess surrounding you gets blurred, but a lot less painful. Agent Porter frequented the place. He sat at the bar and watched me work. Once he took me aside and mentioned that I should "watch the drinking." I told him to mind his own business and our friendship fizzled, doused by one too many gin and tonics.

The Lion's Den saved my sanity on more than one level. First, like I said, the money definitely improved. Second, the wacky staff kept me laughing a lot. We had a series of managers that were really downright crazy.

There was Rodger, a young, good-looking, pot-smoking radical who used to interview potential employees with the following questions:

How often do you change your socks?

What is your favorite ice cream?

How will this busboy/waitress/bartender job lead you closer to your dreams?

Occasionally, he would remove one arm from his suit sleeve to give the impression that he was missing a limb while leading patrons to their table, to increase the amount of what he called "sympathy tips." If a customer acted up in any way, he would approach you at the bar and point to the glass of wine on your tray and ask, "Is that wine for the man over there who's giving you trouble?" If you answered yes, he would repeat as he pointed at him, "That man? Are you sure?" If you responded affirmatively, he would lick his finger, stick it in the wine glass saying, "Here, let me stir that for you.

Then there were the tyrants hired to manage the room—men who had to bolster their egos by treating others like shit. Most of them were alcoholics and our two bartenders, Rich and Tom, knew exactly how to get rid of them. "Don't worry," Tom would say, after seeing one of us mistreated. "He will be gone in less than two weeks," and they both proceeded to ply them with free booze until they inevitably got fired. We went through about twenty managers in the four years I worked there.

And who could forget old Mr. Clark? The waitstaff and bartenders were managing that room, but he was too ancient to realize it. We easily controlled Mr. Clark. My sister Gina, who lived in Oregon, had marital problems and phoned me crying. She wanted to leave her husband. I invited her to come back home to Sable and live with me: I would get her a job in The Lion's Den as a cocktail waitress.

Now, Gina had never been a waitress and didn't know the first thing about serving. She didn't even drink and couldn't tell a Martini from an Old Fashioned. I told poor Mr. Clark that we needed more staff, which of course we didn't, and he agreed to interview her. In the meantime, I had given her a quick course on serving food and how to garnish drinks. We made up a lie of all the places where she had served, including hotels in Las Vegas, for her resume. Mr. Clark agreed to give her a one-night trial.

I warned the bartenders and the chef that my sister didn't have a clue about what she was doing. She proved that easily: spilled a liter of wine all over a table, served dinner to a table that hadn't even ordered it, got her checks so mixed up that she started labeling them. At the top of her checks, in tiny letters she wrote: "Bald", "Mean", "Skinny," Sloppy," names that rivaled the seven dwarfs and identified her customers. When the bartenders noticed her labeled checks, they amused themselves by figuring out which check belonged to which customer. She also took the drink orders from right to left, and Rich and Tom placed them on the bar in that exact order so she would know what drink went where. If a patron ordered out of turn, she would just stop them saying, "I'll get to you in a second. Right now, we'll be going clockwise."

By the end of Gina's first night, Mr. Clark started doubting her ability and went up to Rich at the bar, leaned over and asked quietly, "What do you think of this new girl, Gina?"

Rich replied, with a deadpan face, "Best I ever saw."

Gina got the job.

- Chapter 22 -

Donny and His Dad

After a couple of years, The Lion's Den became the hot spot in town and the place where people came to be seen. Even Nicky had the balls to come in once in a while and would flirt with me. He even attempted to get me in bed with him. I resisted; it was tempting, as I still carried a torch for him way deep down inside. He asked about the kids and mentioned that our oldest son, Donny, wanted to live with him. I refused until Donny turned eighteen and no longer needed my permission.

Donny had always yearned for his father's attention. I think he loved Nicky as much or more than I did. Kids seem to love their parents no matter what. When Donny was a young boy, he followed Nicky around the house, watching his father's every move. All he wanted to do was help his dad.

"Go get me the screwdriver," Nicky would tell him. Donny would scurry into the house, find whatever Nicky had asked for, and present it to him proudly with the biggest smile on his face. So many times, Nicky's response destroyed Donny.

"Not that screwdriver, you little idiot. I said the Phillips screw driver. Listen when I talk to you."

You could see Donny's face drop as he lowered his head and ran to get the right one. When I witnessed this kind of abuse, a big fight would erupt.

"How can you talk to your son that way? All he wants to do is help and please you. Can't you see that?" I would scream at him.

"Don't tell me how to talk to my own son. Keep your big Italian nose out of my business," he yelled back.

Donny moved in with his dad the week after he turned eighteen. He seemed happy to have his father all to himself and was thrilled when Nicky asked him to work for him as a delivery boy. Nicky got into the wholesale business, selling men's clothing and jewelry. He promised to buy Donny a car if he did a good job. In the meantime, Donny delivered most packages by bike.

My brother-in-law, Sean O'Shay, a Sable detective, had been assigned to a drug task force and had been investigating Nicky's brother on suspicion of drug trafficking. Sean had kept surveillance on Frankie for some time and observed Donny picking up a package from his uncle's residence. He slowly followed behind him.

"Hey, Donny, how are you doing, son?" Sean asked, pulling his car alongside the bike.

"Uncle Sean, what's happening?" Donny answered nervously as he hopped off onto the curb.

"You tell me, Donny. What's in the package in your basket there?" he asked condescendingly.

"I don't know. Just making a delivery for my uncle. I work for my dad now but my Uncle Frankie asked me to run an errand."

"Well, that's what has me worried, son. I need to see what's in that package."

There were no lines Nicky and his brother wouldn't cross, including sending my young son on a dangerous delivery like that. No surprise that the package contained an eight-ball of cocaine.

"Uncle Sean, wait," he pleaded, when his uncle unwrapped the package. "This has nothing to do with my father; it's for my Uncle Frankie. I didn't know what was in that package, I swear."

"Wish I could believe you, Donny, but I don't. I've heard rumors of a big drug drop in the next few days. Do you know anything about that?"

"Please, Uncle Sean. Please, my Uncle Frankie will kill me," Donny said, shaken, wiping the tears from his eyes before they could fall.

"Look, the last thing I want to do is take you in, Donny, but I'll have to arrest you right now if you don't cooperate," Sean warned him. "I can leave you and your dad out of this if you help me out here."

Donny caved in and told his Uncle Sean everything he had heard about the date, time, and location of the drop, in exchange for his freedom and to protect his father. Sean carefully rewrapped the package and told Donny to make the delivery then stay away from his Uncle Frankie. Poor kid, he still lives with the guilt that he was responsible for putting his Uncle Frankie behind bars. Not long after that, Donny moved back home and I felt grateful that Sean had influenced him to do so.

That was the second time my brother-in-law Sean had helped me out. The first time, when I was still working for Carlo Russo at Luigi's, he phoned me one morning and told me not to go to work that day.

"Why, Sean? What's going on?" I asked

"There's going to be a raid on the place tonight and you could be in danger," he warned.

I felt afraid to not show up at work for fear that Carlo would suspect I had something to do with what was about to happen, and I told Sean that. He just warned me to be very careful, stay out of the way and as far from Carlo as possible.

That same evening at around 10:00 p.m., the restaurant swarmed with police and detectives. We were all pushed to one side and held in place by twelve policemen. The other cops went directly to the basement to the safe, where they found $300,000 in cash, along with four guns and a silencer. I watched Carlo and his brother cuffed and arrested, put away for the next ten years of their lives.

- The Ladies -

Texting on Thursday, 10 a.m.

Sami, I understand the way you felt about Nicky.
What kind of a man would put his young son
in such danger?

A real bastard, that's what kind.
See, I told you that you would hate him.

Now wait,
I didn't say I hated him.

No, but you're thinking
about it, hey?

- Chapter 23 -
Can't Be All Bad

My sister Gina got to be a pretty good waitress and learned how to be cold yet polite and professional in handling the men who hit on her at The Lion's Den. That is, except for that one particular night.

Gina stood facing the bar with her back to the tables when she felt a hand slip under her short cocktail costume and right into her pants. In shock, she screamed and turned to face two nicely dressed men in their late twenties. She came absolutely unhinged, started punching one of them in the chest screaming, "What the hell do you think you're doing, you filthy asshole?"

He countered with, "What? What? Are you crazy, woman? I didn't do anything."

The manager rushed over between them and held Gina's arms from flailing and told her to calm down and tell him what happened.

"This idiot just stuck his hand in my pants, that's what!" Gina screamed as she tried to hit him again.

The club fell into dead silence. The guys insisted they didn't know what she was talking about. But Gina continued accusing them as she tried to get past the manager, screaming "call the police, call the police!" The manager told the men to leave as he held Gina back, barely able to control her as she attempted to push past him all the way to the elevator. Just as the lift door was about to close, one of the men smiled at her and blew a kiss. I have never before or since seen my sister so angry. It took a shot of gin to calm her down.

Later that night, business got slow, so all the waitresses had been sent home early except for Gina and me. I could hardly keep my eyes open, so Gina told me to go home and she would close the club. At 1:30 a.m., Gina gave last call and started to clean her station. Everyone was gone by the time she took the elevator to the first floor to go home.

When the doors opened onto the deserted lobby, she heard a voice from across the way call out.

"There's the bitch… get her."

It was the same two men who had assaulted her earlier. She jumped out of the elevator and darted through the swinging doors into the darkened upstairs kitchen, ran around the corner and into the tiny time-card booth and ducked down. She held her breath when they followed her in and heard them say, "There must be another way out of here. Let's split up." They ran back through the doors of the kitchen and Gina waited until their footsteps faded, then slowly tiptoed back to the lobby. Just as she peered through a crack, she saw my ex and four of his North Sable thugs walk through the front door of the hotel looking for me. She went running to him crying, "Oh Nicky, thank God."

"Hey, where's Sami? What's wrong, Gina?"

Her words couldn't tumble out fast enough. "They're after me, Nicky. Help me, please, please," Gina pleaded.

"Calm down, babe, who is after you?" Nicky asked.

Just then, the doors to the foyer pushed open and there stood the two men. Gina's arm shot out like a gun as she pointed her trigger finger toward them.

"They are!" she screamed.

For a second, the two men froze, eyes practically popping out of their heads, color melted from their faces, then both tore to the closest exit door and leaped out of the hotel. Nicky hollered to Gina to stay put as he and his buddies charged after them.

Twenty long minutes later, Nicky, followed by one of his buddies, returned wiping blood from his fist.

"What happened, Nicky? Did you find them? Are you alright? Where are the rest of your friends?" Gina asked.

"It's okay. Don't worry, they won't bother you ever again," Nicky replied as he gave her a hug. "C'mon, I'll walk you to your car." He followed her home that night and made sure she got in safely.

The next day, when Gina told me what happened, I searched the morning paper for any murders or assaults. Nothing.

From then on, Gina felt overwhelming gratitude toward my ex-husband. She was convinced that if it wasn't for Nicky that night, she would have been raped or killed or both. And it's probably true. But it bothered me when she'd defend him saying, "The man can't be all bad." But I'm sure Nicky was at least ninety-nine percent rotten.

- Chapter 24 -

Life After Nicky

It's amazing how much your view of yourself improves when you escape the grip of an abusive spouse. I began to see more possibilities for my future. First, I stopped waitressing and became a bartender. The tips were just as good, and the work half as hard. Attending so many of Nicky's trials sparked an interest in law, so I took some introductory classes. After assessing the cost of a law degree, I had to lower my expectations and I finished a course in court reporting.

While attending school, I met Sandy, who was taking a course in real estate law; she owned her own business and we became friends. Over coffee one morning, she started asking questions.

"So, Sami, why court reporting?"

"I found the experience of seeing an actual trial fascinating and it seemed the way to go," I explained.

"Well, do you think you would find the experience of making really good money fascinating?" she joked.

That's how it all began. Sandy hired me once I got my real estate license and taught me the ins and outs of the world of real estate. With her help, it took me about a year and a half to see steady sales, then I started making good money. At last, I left the restaurant business, even though it had served me well. No pun intended.

After working for Sandy for four years, I became her top producer and began to realize how much she was making as my broker. So, I went back to school to get my broker's license and that was no easy feat. It took me five tries to finally pass the test and I was only one question away from passing each time. Of course, they wouldn't tell me which questions I had missed. Maddening! But I finally did it.

I decided to start my own real estate company with Sandy's blessing.

"You go for it, Sami. I'll always be here if it doesn't work, and you can have your job back anytime."

I started my own business, Righteous Realty, working out of my home. My business code, based on excellent service and trust, more than anything, served as an example to my children that hard work and honesty outperforms a life of crime. It didn't take long before I opened my own office and hired several more people, paid off my debts and helped my kids. I started doing all the things I had dreamt about: purchased a home and remodeled it, bought a new wardrobe, ate at nice restaurants and traveled like crazy from New York to Paris to Africa. I felt like I had truly arrived and loved every minute of it.

Seven years after our divorce, Nicky married a younger woman, Bernadette, a dental hygienist. They had a child. She worked full time while he stayed home, ate donuts and cooked an occasional dinner. (Nicky learned how to make tomato sauce and pasta, the extent of his domesticity.)

Nicky never paid a dime of the court-ordered child support for our children. Thankfully, I didn't need his money anymore, but I couldn't let him get away with it and I hired a lawyer. He owed me fifty thousand dollars in back child support but with proof of his unemployment, he only had to pay a hundred dollars a week or face prison again. Not nearly enough, I know, but it felt like a little poke in his side every time I deposited his check.

Nicky had a heart attack in the eighteenth year of his marriage to Bernadette. I never found out if it happened before or after she told him she had met another man and wanted a divorce. I prefer to visualize it happening moments after she told him. Nicky managed to survive the heart attack.

It was a true blessing that Mama took over Katy's care, not only for me but for my children as well. I think Mama loved her more than anyone and Papa went along with the confines that this care created, because he loved Katy too.

Cancer took my oldest sister, Eileen, at age fifty-six. Her death hit all of us hard but it dealt a devastating blow to my parents. Losing a child is not the expected natural order of things. My parents were never the same again.

My younger sister, Gina, married a wonderful man she had met in The Lion's Den. She moved to California, where she still resides.

Old age sidelined Mama when she fell and broke her hip. That event became a major turning point. Who would help care for Katy now that Mama could not? This forced me to make the hardest decision I've ever had to make: I placed Katy in a residential group home without Mama's approval.

After Papa died, Gina and I talked our mother into moving to an assisted-living center. Mama died at age ninety-five after a brief illness. Nicky attended her funeral in a wheelchair, tethered to an oxygen tank. Men seem to age gracefully; that wasn't the case with Nicky. His health took a toll on his once handsome face. Dark circles emphasized his sunken eyes; thinning hair gave prominence to a misshapen skull, and a gray complexion gave new meaning to the phrase, "death warmed over." Yet he still managed to flirt with Sandy (a real estate friend of mine) through Mama's entire service. Nothing like an old fool.

Nicky's ex-wife, Bernadette, came to Mama's funeral out of respect for his children. As she passed through the condolence line, hugging Tina, Donny, and Sonny, she stopped and introduced herself to me. As we shook hands, I introduced her to Katy.

"Bernadette, I don't think you have ever met our daughter Katy," I said as Katy sat silent, looking straight ahead through the fog of her drugs.

"This is Nicky's daughter?" she said, looking shocked. "I didn't know he had four children.

In eighteen years, Nicky had never mentioned to her that Katy even existed.

Bernadette and I stared at one another for a few seconds as our heads nodded knowingly, then we gave each other a tearful embrace.

- Chapter 25 -

Ding Dong

Nicky's health continued to deteriorate, and he asked each of his kids if he could move in with them. They all declined. Even his own siblings wanted nothing to do with him. He landed in a nursing home, where his bitterness grew. Yet, he elicited just enough sympathy and guilt to get his children to purchase most of his medicine and personal items.

The angry old man grew angrier, yelling, "Fuck you" at his caregivers or anyone who tried to be of help to him. Once, Tina went to visit him and left crying after he screamed at her, "What the hell are you doing here? I sure as hell don't need you now." I felt pity for him, mixed with a drop of schadenfreude. Without his good looks and his youthful charms, Nicky no longer had the tools to get what he wanted.

Nicky died six months after Mama. The funeral was small, but most of the mob that was left showed up in their black hats and overcoats, with their little red lions posing in the rear windows of their cars.

During his service, there was a melody running through my brain that I couldn't place. As I exited the church I was humming it, very low, and could not remember the title or the words. Then it popped into my mind and the words from the chorus came out in a whisper: "Ding dong, the witch is dead..." I used a tissue to hide my smile.

There was sadness in my heart, but not for Nicky. It was for that beautiful, naïve young Catholic girl who wasted so many years praying to change her "dream man," hopelessly in love with a lost cause.

- The Ladies -

The 4:14 p.m. Email

To: Lena@gmail.com
From: Sami@hotmail.com
Subject: Sonny

Hi Lena,

You asked me for more information about my youngest boy, Sonny. I think he came through the trauma of our lives the least affected. Perhaps, it is because he is the youngest; he didn't feel the impact of the family dynamics for several years simply because he was too young to understand it. Also, as the baby of the family he got more attention and less was expected of him in regard to Katy's care.

As Sonny grew up and began to understand, he certainly was sympathetic and caring toward his sick older sister. Whenever Katy got a cold, or hurt herself from a fall from a seizure, he would rush to comfort her in any way he could.

Katy had a toy that would play the song "*Raindrops Keep Falling on My Head.*" She drove the family crazy with it-playing it over and over-sometimes even in the middle of the night. Sonny memorized the words to that song and whenever Katy felt badly he would sing that song to her, which almost always brought a smile to her face.

I hope this info helps.

Love,
Sami

- Chapter 26 -

Looking Back

Like a sculptor, life chips away at the unnecessary parts of ourselves in order to create the person we become. I certainly have regrets but have forgiven myself for past mistakes, the biggest being the years I stayed with Nicky. I'm trying to pardon Nicky, too, but I'm not quite there yet and still feel anger when I think of him. He's my daily practice in forgiveness; apparently, I'm a slow learner.

It is difficult to pinpoint Nicky's contributions to our children's lives; but one definite contribution came through his genes. All my children are gorgeous. I mean seriously, head-turning, drop-dead gorgeous!

I am very proud of my achievements and those of my children. We all survived.

Katy is now in a residential home shared by three other residents and two wonderful caregivers. She has her own bedroom and all her needs are met. Still, today her health presents some real challenges. She is showing signs of cerebral palsy and still suffers from seizure disorder. Recently she suffered onsets of pneumonia twice. I never stop worrying about her. Yet she warms my heart when I take her out for our weekly visit and ask her if she wants to go back to the home; her face lights up with a big smile and she responds with "Peez!" This reassures me that she loves the people who take care of her and where she is living. That alone gives me so much peace.

Tina has two beautiful children from her first marriage. She is now remarried and has a successful career as a physical therapist. She has always been stunning with her blond hair, blue eyes and perfect figure. As the oldest of my children, she had to grow up too fast. She helped babysit her siblings and shared a room with Katy for many years. I often wonder how many times in the middle of the night she was awakened by the sound of Katy's seizures. I will always be grateful to her for the caregiver part she played in our family, and proud of the strong woman she has become.

Donny managed to break the chains of addiction that clouded his life for a number of years. He moved to New Mexico to get away from his circle of "friends" in North Sable and get clean and sober. He never married or had children. He started his own construction company, built a wonderful home for himself, and pulls in a six-figure salary. On a recent visit to Sable, he went to visit Katy and sang songs that he used to sing to her when they were children. He always did love to make her laugh and he sure knew how. Her giggles assured us that she hadn't forgotten her big brother.

Sonny married his second wife a few years after his divorce. She came with a ready-made family including two children and a grandchild that Sonny has embraced as his own. Like the rest of my children, he is self-employed. He owns an electrical inspection business. Whenever we discuss our lives, he always says, "I wouldn't change a thing. It made me what I am today... strong!"

All a mother ever wants for her children is that they become good contributing citizens, provide for themselves and their families, and have some semblance of peace and happiness, right? My children have done that and I am so proud of them. My Katy is in a safe environment with people who care for and love her. What more could I want?

- *The Ladies* -

The 3rd Trip to Vegas

During the two years that it took Lena to write Sami's story, vows between the ladies were broken: the promise to talk every Thursday night, the rule to write at least an hour every day, the mantra "We will get published" sworn to be repeated out loud five times a day, the commitment to tell the truth and only the truth, and the agreement to meet in Las Vegas every three months. In spite of the broken pledges, Lena and Sami finished the book and met in Las Vegas for a final read-through.

After arriving in Vegas, the first order of business involved tequila at the 3535 Bar at The Linq Hotel where it had all started.

"Let's toast," Sami proposed, holding up her double shot of Patrón Silver as Streisand's recording of "*My Man*" from *Funny Girl* poured out of the loud speakers. "To both of us, dear cousin, for extracting this damn story out of my head, once and for all. I feel like I've had a complete high colonic."

"Wait, would you listen to the song that is playing?" Lena interrupted.

"Shit, how synchronistic can it be?" Sami asked as they both started singing along with Barbra.

All my life is just despair, but I don't care.

When he takes me in his arms, the world is bright… all right.

Then, the final lyric:

For whatever my man is, I am his forever more.

Sami looked up and shouted at the ceiling, "You bastard, Nicky. I loved you." Realizing her mistake of looking toward heaven, she leaned to one side and spoke directly toward the floor and repeated, "You bastard, Nicky. I loved you." Everyone at the bar laughed and applauded, calling out, "You tell him, baby" or "Way to go, lady" followed by "Give those two ladies whatever they are drinking and put it on my tab."

The cousins clinked glasses through two more rounds, then giggled all the way to the room. Lena pulled out the two copies of the book and they lay on the bed, heads propped up on the large pillows, taking turns reading each chapter out loud with their thick tequila tongues. Tears flowed after almost every chapter, with Lena reaching over to hug Sami, saying, "I'm so sorry that you had to live through this." And Sami responding, "Thank you, honey, me too. I'm so sorry for me too."

Sami fell asleep before they reached the final chapter. Lena tucked her into bed without sharing her news, then fell asleep with the copy of their book and the letter from the agent clutched to her chest.

Acknowledgements

I want to acknowledge the people who helped bring this story to life especially.

Phyllis Borelli and her children for the inspiration. Clive Pollard and Chimene Pollard for their patient listening through each chapter, Annie Gladue for making publishing possible, for her organizational and writing skills and encouragement, and especially for my Dragon Buster.

I am grateful to my friends MaryAnne Gackle and Mary Jo Trusso for reading and sharing their expertise in the field of psychology.

Thank you to the members of our writing group: Scott Peeler for his expertise in editing and writing, Julia Tranchina for her gentle critiques and Dianne Saichek.

Thanks to Jackie Gallanagh and Glenda Pollard for reading and for their suggestions, Elaine Bartlett for all of her insight and Nita Gill for her encouragement and suggestions.

And Diane Pinkard for all the hours of listening.

I would also like to thank Maggie Shen, Martha Cooley and Colleen Olle.

From the bottom of my heart, I feel privileged to have you all in my life.

Sonny's Drawing – Age Seven